NUMBER CORNER
TEACHERS GUIDE — VOLUME TWO

BRIDGES IN MATHEMATICS 4

written by
Allyn Fisher

illustrated by
Tyson Smith

Published by
The **MATH LEARNING CENTER**
Salem, Oregon

ISBN 9781602620094

B4NCTG-2

Number Corner Grade 4 Teachers Guide Volume Two

The Number Corner Grade 4 Package consists of—

Number Corner Teachers Guide Volume One

Number Corner Teachers Guide Volume Two

Number Corner Blacklines

Number Corner Overheads

Number Corner Student Book Blacklines

Number Corner Calendar Markers

Number Corner Components

Number Corner Manipulatives

The Math Learning Center, PO Box 12929, Salem, Oregon 97309. Tel. 1 800 575–8130.

© 2007 by The Math Learning Center

All rights reserved.

Prepared for publication on Macintosh Desktop Publishing system.

Printed in the United States of America.

QP480, QP537 and QP539   B4NCTG-2

P0907   10/07

Number Corner is a year's worth of skill-building lessons and assessments. A key component of the *Bridges in Mathematics* K–5 curriculum, it can also be used to supplement other mathematics curricula.

The Math Learning Center is a nonprofit organization serving the education community. Our mission is to inspire and enable individuals to discover and develop their mathematical confidence and ability. We offer innovative and standards-based professional development, curriculum, materials, and resources to support learning and teaching. To find out more, visit us at www.mathlearningcenter.org.

This project was supported, in part, by the National Science Foundation. Opinions expressed are those of the authors and not necessarily those of the Foundation.

ISBN 9781602620094

January

February

March

April

May & June

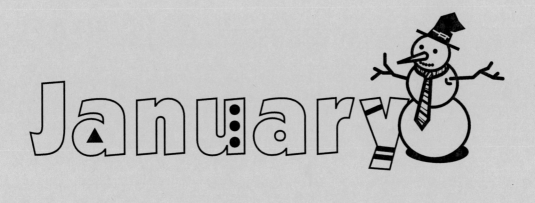

Tile Sampling Record Sheet

Day	Tile Drawn	Daily Total Blue	Daily Total Red
1		2	3
2		1	4
3		1	4
4		1	4
5		2	3
6		1	4
7		1	4
8		1	4
9		1	4
10		2	3
11		2	3
12		1	4
13		2	3
14		2	3
15		2	3
16		1	4
17		2	3

Calendar Collector

January

Sunday	Monday	Tuesday	Wednesday	Thursday	Friday	Saturday
						1
2		4	3	6	7	8
9	10	11	12	13	14	15
16	17					

Calendar Grid

January Calendar Record Sheet

Date	Time	a.m./p.m.	Elapsed Time — Between today and the day before	Elapsed Time — Total time elapsed since the 1st
1/1	12:00	a.m.		
1/2	1:10	a.m.	1 hr. 10 min.	1 hr. 10 min.
1/3	2:20	a.m.	1 hr. 10 min.	2 hr. 20 min.
1/4	3:30	a.m.	1 hr. 10 min.	3 hr. 30 min.
1/5	4:40	a.m.	1 hr. 10 min.	4 hr. 40 min.
1/6	5:50	a.m.	1 hr. 10 min.	5 hr. 50 min.
1/7	7:00	a.m.	1 hr. 10 min.	7 hours
1/8	8:20	a.m.	1 hr. 20 min.	8 hr. 20 min.
1/9	9:40	a.m.	1 hr. 20 min.	9 hr. 40 min.
1/10	11:00	a.m.	1 hr. 20 min.	11 hours
1/11	12:20	p.m.	1 hr. 20 min.	12 hr. 20 min.
1/12	1:40	p.m.	1 hr. 20 min.	13 hr. 40 min.
1/13	3:00	p.m.	1 hr. 20 min.	15 hours
1/14	4:30	p.m.	1 hr. 30 min.	16 hr. 30 min.
1/15	6:00	p.m.	1 hr. 30 min.	18 hours
1/16	7:30	p.m.	1 hr. 30 min.	19 hr. 30 min.
1/17	9:00	p.m.	1 hr. 30 min.	21 hours

January Overhead NC 5.1

Quick Facts Worksheet

What's your multiplier?	How many minutes?	Number correct
2	1–2	

1 Multiply each number in the grid by your multiplier. Write each product in the box.

10^5	14^7	6^3	12^6	2^1	0^0	4^2	20^{10}
8^4	12^6	22^{11}	18^9	24^{12}	16^8	8^4	10^5
12^6	20^{10}	4^2	14^7	8^4	2^1	18^9	6^3
18^9	14^7	24^{12}	4^2	22^{11}	2^1	16^8	20^{10}
22^{11}	24^{12}	6^3	8^4	14^7	12^6	10^5	18^9

2 Choose 10 *different* products from above (except 0) and record them in the 10 boxes below. Then divide each by your multiplier.

$2)\overline{10}$ $\quad$ $2)\overline{4}$ $\quad$ $2)\overline{8}$ $\quad$ $2)\overline{12}$ $\quad$ $2)\overline{6}$

$2)\overline{16}$ $\quad$ $2)\overline{14}$ $\quad$ $2)\overline{18}$ $\quad$ $2)\overline{20}$ $\quad$ $2)\overline{24}$

Computational Fluency

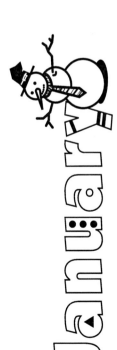

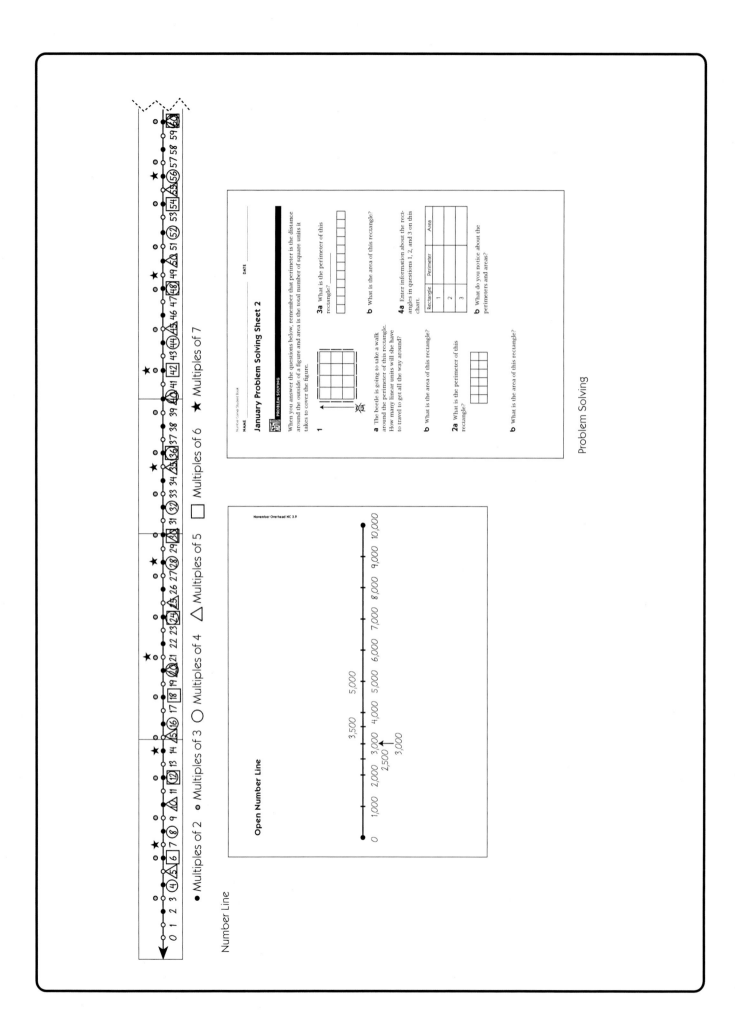

Number Line

• Multiples of 2   ◦ Multiples of 3   ○ Multiples of 4   △ Multiples of 5   ☐ Multiples of 6   ★ Multiples of 7

Open Number Line

Problem Solving

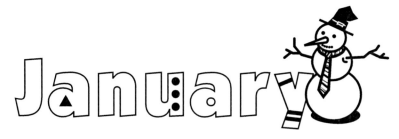

What's Going to Happen in January?

Much of the mathematical thinking this month revolves around making predictions and deductions on the basis of emergent information. To do this, students use a variety of strategies throughout the month. As always, they use emerging patterns on the Calendar Grid to make predictions about future markers. In the Calendar Collector Workout, they will use the process of sampling, a procedure that may be familiar to many fourth graders, to deduce how many red and blue tile are in a closed bag. In the Number Line Workouts, students strategically narrow down a range of numbers to identify a single secret number between 0 and 10,000 selected by the teacher. In all cases, students use their number sense and problem solving skills to make accurate predictions and deductions based upon known information.

Calendar Grid

The markers this month feature analog clocks, which show times that get later each day according to a predictable pattern. For the first six days, the time increases by 1 hour and 10 minutes each day. For the next 6 days, the time increases by 1 hour and 20 minutes each day. This pattern continues every six days throughout the month, so that by the end of the month, each new time is 1 hour and 50 minutes later than the last. The class keeps track of the times and elapsed time on a record sheet. Students will discuss the grid and the record sheet at least twice this month and will work independently or in pairs to complete four pages in their Student Books. The pages ask them to make observations about the emerging patterns and predict what future markers will look like. In doing so, students practice telling time and calculating elapsed time.

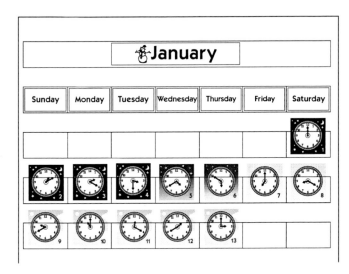

January Calendar Record Sheet				
Date	Time	a.m./p.m.	Elapsed Time	
			Between today and the day before	Total time elapsed since the 1st
1/1	12:00	a.m.		
1/2	1:10	a.m.	1 hr. 10 min.	1 hr. 10 min.
1/3	2:20	a.m.	1 hr. 10 min.	2 hr. 20 min.
1/4	3:30	a.m.	1 hr. 10 min.	3 hr. 30 min.
1/5	4:40	a.m.	1 hr. 10 min.	4 hr. 40 min.
1/6	5:50	a.m.	1 hr. 10 min.	5 hr. 50 min.
1/7	7:00	a.m.	1 hr. 10 min.	7 hours
1/8	8:20	a.m.	1 hr. 20 min.	8 hr. 20 min.
1/9	9:40	a.m.	1 hr. 20 min.	9 hr. 40 min.
1/10	11:00	a.m.	1 hr. 20 min.	11 hours
1/11	12:20	p.m.	1 hr. 20 min.	12 hr. 20 min.
1/12	1:40	p.m.	1 hr. 20 min.	13 hr. 40 min.
1/13	3:00	p.m.	1 hr. 20 min.	15 hours

Calendar Collector

The focus of the Calendar Collector shifts in January from measurement to probability and data. Early in the month, students are presented with a bag containing 9 game markers, some of which are red and some of which are blue. The challenge is to figure out how many of each color are likely to be in the bag without taking them all out and looking at them. This is accomplished using a technique called sampling in which 1 marker is drawn out of the sack, its color recorded, and then the marker returned to the sack. The class collects 5 samples each day for a total of 155 samples for the month. Based on the data they collect and record, students make conjectures about the contents of the bag at mid-month and again at the end of the month.

Computational Fluency

While it's important for students to develop and use strategies such as double-doubles, clock facts, and so on, there comes a time in every fourth graders' life when the multiplication and related division facts are best committed to memory. To this end, you'll introduce a new routine called Quick Facts in which students get to choose which set of multiplication facts to work with each week. Once they have demonstrated fluency with a set of facts, they can move on to a new set of facts of their choice.

A student is considered fluent with a set of facts if she can complete 40 multiplication facts in that group in 2 minutes. This is a rate of 3 seconds per fact. Although similar to timed testing, Quick Facts is not a test or a competition. Students maintain control because they choose their own sets of facts each time and track their own progress. This routine will continue for a few months to give students time to demonstrate fluency with facts from 2×12 to 12×12.

January Blackline NC 5.6 Run 4 class sets.

NAME _____ DATE _____

Quick Facts Worksheet

What's your multiplier?	How many minutes?	Number correct
2	1–2	35

1 Multiply each number in the grid by your multiplier. Write each product in the box.

5	7	3	6	1	0	2	10
10	16	6	12	2	0	4	20
4	6	11	9	12	8	4	5
8	12	24	17	24	16	8	10
6	10	2	7	8	1	9	3
12	20	4	14	16	2	18	6
9	7	12	2	11	0	8	10
18	14	24	4	24	0	16	20
11	12	3	4	7	6	5	9
22	24	6	8	14	12	10	17

2 Choose 10 *different* products from above (except 0) and record them in the 10 boxes below. Then divide each by your multiplier.

$$2\overline{)10}\;\;5 \qquad 2\overline{)4}\;\;2 \qquad 2\overline{)8}\;\;4 \qquad 2\overline{)12}\;\;6 \qquad 2\overline{)6}\;\;3$$

$$2\overline{)2}\;\;1 \qquad 2\overline{)20}\;\;10 \qquad 2\overline{)0}\;\;0 \qquad 2\overline{)24}\;\;11 \qquad 2\overline{)17}\;\;9$$

Number Corner Student Book

NAME _____ DATE _____

Quick Facts Tracking Sheet

COMPUTATIONAL FLUENCY

When you get back your Quick Facts Worksheet from last week, look at your score. Record the date you completed the sheet, the time it took you, and the number of facts you got correct on the table below. If it took you more than 2 minutes or you got fewer than 38 facts correct, write "no" in the last column and use that same multiplier again. If you completed 38 or more facts correctly in 1–2 minutes, write "yes" in the last column and choose another multiplier.

Cross out each number as you master the set of facts for that multiplier.

2   3   4   5   6   7   8   9   10   11   12

Multiplier	Date	Time	Number Correct	Mastered? (at least 38 correct in 1–2 minutes)
2	Jan. 7	1–2 mins	35	No

Problem Solving

In the Problem Solving Workouts this month, students work on a new sheet of problems each week. The problems this month ask students to find the perimeter and area of rectangles, compute with money, find the missing elements in patterned sequences of numbers, calculate elapsed time, and solve a variety of story problems.

Number Line

This month, student helpers enter a new number on the Number Line for each day they are in school and mark the multiples of 2, 3, 4, 5, 6, and 7. Whole-group workouts are spent discussing the new numbers and multiples of 7, playing Round & Add to the nearest 1000, and playing a new game called What's My Number?. Both games provide students with opportunities to read, order, round, and compare 3- and 4-digit numbers. In What's My Number?, the teacher chooses a secret number between 0 and 10,000. The students take turns guessing the secret number. The teacher identifies each guess as greater than or less than the secret number, allowing students to quickly "zero in" on the secret number on the open number line.

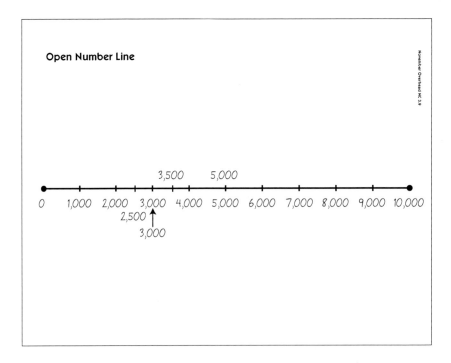

After each team has made 2 guesses, they can see that the secret number is between 3,000 and 3,500.

Assessment & Support Activities

This month includes the second of four quarterly basic skills checkups. January's checkup focuses on basic multiplication facts; making conversions between inches, feet, and yards as well as cups, quarts, and gallons; calculating area and perimeter; figuring elapsed time; multi-digit addition, subtraction, multiplication, and division; and connecting common fractions and decimals. This checkup, like the other three checkups this year, is optional. However, we find it provides a good summary of what students know and can do with regard to basic or "life-skills" math at this point in the school year, and also provides an opportunity to practice test-taking skills.

January Blackline NC A 5.1
NAME _____ DATE _____

Number Corner Checkup 2 page 1 of 4

1 Solve these multiplication facts.

2 × 9	5 × 3	7 × 6	3 × 7	4 × 5	6 × 7	8 × 2
3 × 9	6 × 3	5 × 4	4 × 7	9 × 6	8 × 3	7 × 8
9 × 7	7 × 3	4 × 4	6 × 6	5 × 5	0 × 6	1 × 7
4 × 1	9 × 8	3 × 9	8 × 8	5 × 7	10 × 7	7 × 9

January Blackline NC A 5.2
NAME _____ DATE _____

Number Corner Checkup 2 page 2 of 4

2 How many inches are in 3 feet?

6 ○   18 ○   36 ○   100 ○

3 How many feet are in 5 yards?

10 ○   15 ○   30 ○   50 ○

4 How many cups are in a gallon?

4 ○   8 ○   12 ○   16 ○

5 Adam and his dad made 20 cups of strawberry jam. How many quart containers will they need to hold the jam?

2 ○   4 ○   5 ○   10 ○

6

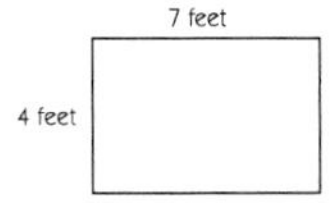

[rectangle: 7 feet across top, 4 feet on left side]

a What is the perimeter of this rectangle?

b What is the area of this rectangle?

January Blackline NC A 5.3
NAME _____ DATE _____

Number Corner Checkup 2 page 3 of 4

8 Circle the best estimate

900
1000
1,050
1,100

| 240 |
| 355 |
| 399 |
| + 102 |
| ? |

9 The museum had 347 visitors on Saturday morning. What is this number rounded to the nearest 100?

300 ○   400 ○   500 ○   600 ○

10 Do all three of the problems below. Use numbers and/or sketches to show how you got your answers.

a $2.53
   + $3.47

b 145
   226
   + 175

c 317
   − 209

11 Choose one of the multiplication problems below. Circle the one that seems best for you—not too hard and not too easy. Find the answer in *two different ways* and show your work for both ways.

12	20	25	36	51
× 4	× 9	× 7	× 5	× 8

January Blackline NC A 5.4
NAME _____ DATE _____

Number Corner Checkup 2 page 4 of 4

12 Choose one of the division problems below. Circle the one that seems best for you—not too hard and not too easy. Find the answer and be sure to show all your work using numbers, sketches, and words to show how you got your answer.

$7)\overline{21}$ $8)\overline{24}$ $3)\overline{75}$ $3)\overline{63}$ $6)\overline{94}$

13 This picture shows some things about 3 quarters. Circle the statements that are true.

a Together, 3 quarters make $\frac{3}{4}$ of a dollar.

b Together, 3 quarters make $\frac{75}{100}$ of a dollar.

c Together, 3 quarters make $7.50

d Together, 3 quarters make $0.75

e Together, 3 quarters make $75.00

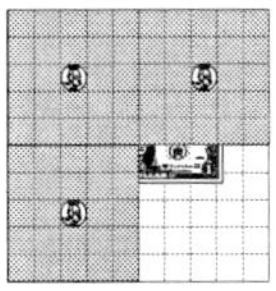

14 There are five $1 bills in each of the stacks below.

a Write a multiplication sentence that tells about the total number of dollars.

We suggest that you administer the checkup at the end of the month, or even very early in February, as it may provide information that is timely and useful to you in writing second quarter report cards. After reviewing students' responses to the items on the checkup, you can assign Support Activities as needed for children to work on at school or at home. At the end of the assessment write-up, we have recommended specific activities that may be helpful. You'll find all Support Activities in their own section at the end of the Number Corner Blacklines.

Planning for January

You can use the planning guide below as shown or adapt it to fit the needs of your students and schedule. You can use this planning guide and the week-by-week write-ups to complete a day-by-day planner (Blackline NC 1.1) for the month.

JANUARY PLANNING GUIDE							
Key ★ = Discuss ☆ = Update SB = Number Corner Student Book	MON	TUES	WED	THURS	FRI	SB	
Calendar Grid, pp. 186–190 Night & Day • determining elapsed time • extending number patterns that grow by common differences	★	☆	☆	☆	★	pp. 47 and 48, 57 and 58	
Calendar Collector, pp. 191–196 Sampling • predicting and representing all possible outcomes • conducting a probability experiment • constructing, reading, and interpreting bar graphs	☆	★	☆	☆	☆	pp. 49 and 59	
Computational Fluency, pp. 197–201 Quick Facts • fluently using multiplication facts through 12 × 12 • developing efficient strategies for solving basic division facts			★			pp. 50–54	
Problem Solving, pp. 202–204 Time, Perimeter, Patterns & Money • multiplying and dividing 2- and 3-digit numbers by 1-digit numbers • adding and subtracting decimals to hundredths using money amounts • extending number patterns that grow by common differences • developing strategies for finding the perimeter and area of rectangles • determining elapsed time				★		pp. 46, 55, 56, and 60	
Number Line, pp. 205–210 Multiples of 7 & Games with Numbers to 10,000 • rounding 3- and 4-digit whole numbers to the nearest 1,000 • exploring factors of whole numbers through 100	☆	☆	☆	☆	★		
Assessment, pp. 211–213 Number Corner Checkup 2	Give this assessment during the last week of January or first week of February. (Blacklines NC A 5.1–5.4)						
Support, pp. 214 Elapsed Time, Basic Multiplication and Division	Use after Number Corner Checkup 2 Assessment. (Blacklines NC S 10.1–17.8)						

Materials You'll Need for January

MANIPULATIVES & MATERIALS

Manipulatives
- Calendar Grid pocket chart
- half-class set of student clocks
- game markers
- dice numbered 1–6 for each pair of students (optional)
- 2 dice, marked 4–9
- plastic or real coins
- calculators
- large Judy clock or other geared clock (optional)
- one-third class set of base ten piece (optional, Use Blackline NC 1.9 if needed.)
- one-third class set of money value pieces (optional, Use Blackline NC 1.10–1.12 if needed.)

Number Corner Calendar Markers
- Day, Month, and Year markers
- Night & Day calendar markers

Number Corner Components
- Number Line

General Materials
- pointer (such as a yard or meter stick)
- red and blue crayons
- colored pencils in red and blue (optional)
- overhead pens
- a few blank overhead transparencies
- chart paper (optional)
- piece of paper to mask parts of the overhead when necessary
- a few small slips of scratch paper
- paper lunch bag or small gift bag

BLACKLINES & OVERHEADS

Number Corner Overheads
NC 3.9	Open Number Line
NC 5.1	Quick Facts Worksheet
NC 5.2	Quick Facts Tracking Sheet
NC 5.3	January Problem Solving Sheet 1
NC 5.4	Sampling Data Chart
NC 5.5	January Problem Solving Sheet 2
NC 5.6	January Problem Solving Sheet 3
NC 5.7	January Problem Solving Sheet 4

Number Corner Blacklines
NC 1.1	Monthly Planner Template (1 copy, optional)
NC 1.9	Base Ten Pieces (one-third class set if needed)
NC 1.10–1.12	Money Value Pieces (one-third class set if needed)
NC 1.13	Paper Bills (if needed)
NC 4.9	Open Number Line (class set, optional)
NC 5.1 & 5.2	January Calendar Grid Record Sheet, pages 1 and 2 (1 copy each, trimmed, taped together, and posted beside the Calendar Grid)
NC 5.3 & 5.4	Sampling Record Sheet, pages 1 and 2 (1 copy of each sheet, trimmed, taped together, and posted on the display board)
NC 5.5	Multiplication Facts Class Checklist (1 or 2 copies)
NC 5.6	Quick Facts Worksheet (4 class sets)

Number Corner Assessment Blacklines
NC A 5.1–5.4	Number Corner Checkup 2, pages 1–4
NC A 5.5 & 5.6	Number Corner Checkup 2 Class Checklist, pages 1 and 2 (2 or 3 copies as needed, optional)

Number Corner Student Book
page 46	January Problem Solving Sheet 1
pages 47 & 48	Night & Day, pages 1 and 2
page 49	Mid-Month Sampling Data
page 50	Quick Facts Tracking Sheet
pages 51–54	Roll 5 (optional)
page 55	January Problem Solving Sheet 2
page 56	January Problem Solving Sheet 3
pages 57 & 58	The Twins' School Day, pages 1 and 2
page 59	End of the Month Sampling Data
page 60	January Problem Solving Sheet 4

January Calendar Grid

CALENDAR GRID

Night & Day

Overview

The markers this month feature analog clocks that show times that get later each day according to a predictable pattern. Students add a new marker to the grid each day and keep track of all the times and elapsed time between markers on a record sheet. Students discuss the grid and the record sheet as a whole group twice this month and work independently or in pairs to complete four pages in their Student Books, on which they make observations about the emerging patterns and predict what future markers will look like.

Frequency

Update the Calendar Grid each day and share observations and predictions or complete a Student Book page once a week.

Skills & Concepts

★ determining elapsed time

★ adding time and making the necessary conversions between minutes and hours

★ describing, extending, and making verbal and written generalizations about number patterns to make predictions and solve problems

★ extending number patterns that grow by common differences

You'll need

★ January Calendar Grid Record Sheet, pages 1 and 2 (Blacklines NC 5.1 and 5.2, 1 copy each, trimmed, taped together, and posted beside the Calendar Grid)

★ Night & Day, pages 1 and 2 (Number Corner Student Book, pages 47 and 48)

★ The Twins' School Day, pages 1 and 2 (Number Corner Student Book, pages 57 and 58)

★ Day, Month, and Year markers

★ Night & Day calendar markers

★ Calendar Grid pocket chart

★ half-class set of student clocks

★ large Judy clock or other geared clock (optional)

Week 1 Introducing the New Markers & Record Sheet

Before the first workout, display the January Calendar Grid Record Sheet beside the Calendar Grid and then display all markers up to, but not including, today's marker. To begin, ask students to share observations and predictions about the posted markers. Make student clocks available so children can use

Calendar Grid Night & Day (cont.)

them to show the times and calculate the elapsed time between markers. You may also find it helpful to use a large geared clock to demonstrate how the position of the hour hand changes as the minute hand moves around the clock face.

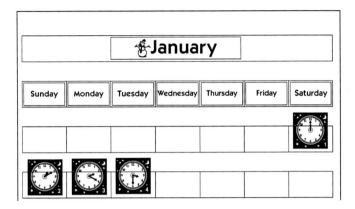

After they have shared observations, ask students to go back and read the times on each clock out loud as you record them on the Calendar Grid Record Sheet, along with the dates. Record a.m. or p.m. for each marker, and explain the two abbreviations to students if needed. Then ask students to tell you how much time has passed between successive markers, and record those amounts of time on the record sheet as well. You'll also need to have students determine a running total of the elapsed time for each date. On the whiteboard, record the process of adding the amounts of elapsed time.

January Calendar Record Sheet				
			Elapsed Time	
Date	Time	a.m./p.m.	Between today and the day before	Total time elapsed since the 1st
1/1	12:00	a.m.		
1/2	1:10	a.m.	1 hr. 10 min.	1 hr. 10 min.
1/3	2:20	a.m.	1 hr. 10 min.	2 hr. 20 min.
1/4	3:30	a.m.	1 hr. 10 min.	3 hr. 30 min.

$$\begin{array}{r} 1\text{ hour} \quad 10\text{ minutes} \\ +\ 1\text{ hour} \quad 10\text{ minutes} \\ \hline 2\text{ hours} \quad 20\text{ minutes} \end{array}$$

$$\begin{array}{r} 2\text{ hours} \quad 20\text{ minutes} \\ +\ 1\text{ hour} \quad 10\text{ minutes} \\ \hline 3\text{ hours} \quad 30\text{ minutes} \end{array}$$

Finally, if it hasn't already come up in discussion, ask students to predict what time will be shown on today's marker and explain their predictions. Then, have a volunteer post today's marker, and record the necessary information on the record sheet. Also invite students to make predictions about future markers.

Calendar Grid Night & Day (cont.)

Week 2 Completing the First Student Book Pages

Sometime between January 10 and 12, have students complete pages 47 and 48 in their Number Corner Student Books. The pages ask them to analyze the first ten markers, make predictions about the 13th marker, and describe any patterns they have noticed so far.

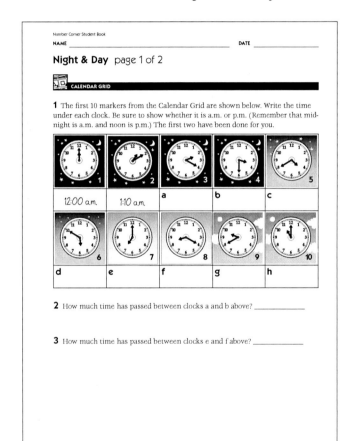

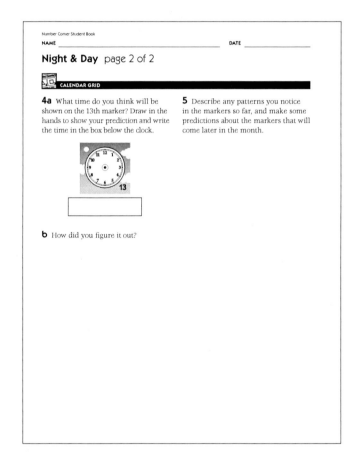

Week 3 Discussing the Calendar Grid and Record Sheet

Open the third workout by asking students to share observations and predictions about the Calendar Grid and record sheet. Make student clocks available so they can show some of the times as the discussion unfolds.

By this point in the month, many students will have noticed that the amount of time elapsed from one marker to the next increases by another 10 minutes every sixth day, not counting the first of the month. For 6 days, then, the clocks move ahead an hour and 10 minutes each day. For another 6 days, they move ahead an hour and 20 minutes each day. For another 6 days, they move ahead an hour and 30 minutes each day. This continues so that by the end of the month, the clocks are progressing an hour and 50 minutes each day.

Calendar Grid Night & Day (cont.)

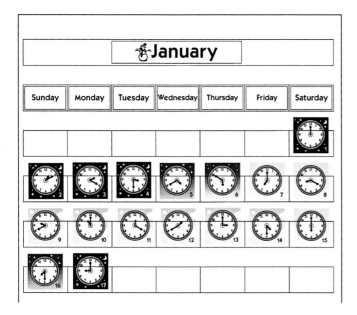

January Calendar Record Sheet				
Date	Time	a.m./p.m.	Elapsed Time	
			Between today and the day before	Total time elapsed since the 1st
1/1	12:00	a.m.		
1/2	1:10	a.m.	1 hr. 10 min.	1 hr. 10 min.
1/3	2:20	a.m.	1 hr. 10 min.	2 hr. 20 min.
1/4	3:30	a.m.	1 hr. 10 min.	3 hr. 30 min.
1/5	4:40	a.m.	1 hr. 10 min.	4 hr. 40 min.
1/6	5:50	a.m.	1 hr. 10 min.	5 hr. 50 min.
1/7	7:00	a.m.	1 hr. 10 min.	7 hours
1/8	8:20	a.m.	1 hr. 20 min.	8 hr. 20 min.
1/9	9:40	a.m.	1 hr. 20 min.	9 hr. 40 min.
1/10	11:00	a.m.	1 hr. 20 min.	11 hours
1/11	12:20	p.m.	1 hr. 20 min.	12 hr. 20 min.
1/12	1:40	p.m.	1 hr. 20 min.	13 hr. 40 min.
1/13	3:00	p.m.	1 hr. 20 min.	15 hours
1/14	4:30	p.m.	1 hr. 30 min.	16 hr. 30 min.
1/15	6:00	p.m.	1 hr. 30 min.	18 hours
1/16	7:30	p.m.	1 hr. 30 min.	19 hr. 30 min.
1/17	9:00	p.m.	1 hr. 30 min.	21 hours

Students' observations and predictions may lead to a deep discussion about elapsed time and the patterns on the grid. If not, select questions from the list below to elicit further insights and debate. As always, have students justify their thinking and explain their reasoning, using their student clocks (or large geared clock if you have one) to make calculations and show their thinking as needed.

- How have the colored backgrounds for the clocks changed through the month so far, and why? (They indicate the shift from night to day in North America during the winter. Some students may notice that there are fewer clocks with daytime backgrounds than there are clocks with nighttime and dawn or dusk backgrounds. Ask them if this would be the case if the times were shown for a summer month. (It would not, because it gets dark much later in the summer months.))
- What time will the clock show on January 19? (12:00 midnight or 12 a.m.) How do you know?
- What time will the clock show next Monday? How do you know?
- There are 24 hours in a day, and the day is usually said to start directly after midnight. Will a full day pass on our calendar this month? (Yes, starting 1 second after the time shown on January 1 and ending 1 second before the time shown on January 19.)
- What activities take most of your time in a period of 24 hours?
- Look very carefully at the numbers that have been entered so far in the "Total Time Elapsed" column. Can you spot any patterns? Explain why those patterns occur. (There are many patterns to be found. Some students

Calendar Grid Night & Day (cont.)

may notice that the hours and minutes entered in that column match the times on the clocks through January 11. Others may discover that the pattern shifts every six days in conjunction with the increase in elapsed time.)

Week 4 Completing the Second Pair of Student Book Pages

Pages 57 and 58 provide more practice telling time and determining elapsed time. Make student clocks available for students to use if they want to. If time permits, have students share and compare their strategies and solutions for the last two problems, either in pairs or as a whole group.

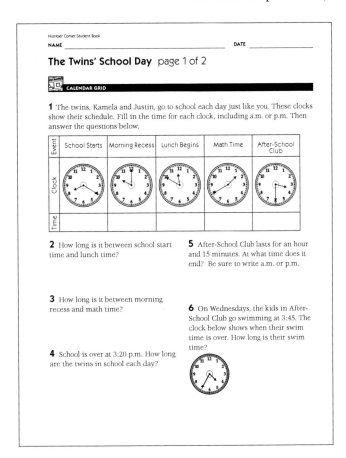

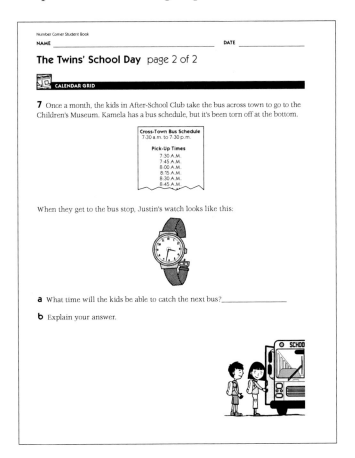

January Calendar Collector

CALENDAR COLLECTOR

Sampling

STUDENT BOOK

Overview

This month, the focus of the Calendar Collector shifts from measurement to probability and data. The teacher puts 9 red and blue game markers in a paper bag, and students are challenged to figure out how many of each color are in the bag without looking. They do this using a technique called sampling, in which they pull 1 marker out of the bag, record its color, and then return it to the bag. The class takes 5 samples for each day of the month including weekends. Based on the data, students make predictions about the contents of the bag at mid-month and again at the end of the month.

Frequency

Update the data daily, and share observations and predictions about the data as a whole group once or twice a week.

Skills & Concepts

★ predicting and representing all possible outcomes for a simple probability situation in an organized way

★ conducting a probability experiment; systematically collecting and recording data; drawing, supporting, and communicating conclusions based on data collected

★ constructing, reading, and interpreting bar graphs

★ exploring basic concepts of sampling, including the fact that larger samples yield better results

★ describing the probability of various outcomes or events

You'll need

★ Sampling Data Chart (Overhead NC 5.4)

★ Sampling Record Sheet, pages 1 and 2 (Blacklines NC 5.3 and 5.4, 1 copy of each sheet, trimmed, taped together, and posted on the display board)

★ Mid-Month Sampling Data (Number Corner Student Book, page 49)

★ End of the Month Sampling Data (Number Corner Student Book, page 59)

★ 6 red game markers and 3 blue game markers placed in a paper lunch bag or small gift bag

★ red and blue crayons

★ chart paper (optional)

....

Advance Preparation If you place the game markers in a gift bag with handles, you may want to hang it beside the record sheet on the display board. If you use a paper lunch bag instead, you may need to replace it with a new one several times during the month.

....

Calendar Collector Sampling (cont.)

....

Week 1 Introducing the Sampling Experiment

Introduce this month's Calendar Collector by holding up the bag you've prepared and telling students that there are 9 game markers in it. Some are red
and some are blue, and the challenge this month will be to determine how
many of each color are likely to be in the bag without dumping them all out
and looking at them.

Ask students to list all the possible combinations of 9 markers, some of which
are red and some of which are blue. As students suggest the various combinations, list them on the board or on a piece of chart paper where they can be
displayed for the month.

Possible Combinations of Red and Blue

1 red, 8 blue
2 red, 7 blue
3 red, 6 blue
4 red, 5 blue
5 red, 4 blue
6 red, 3 blue
7 red, 2 blue
8 red, 1 blue

Explain that they will use the technique of sampling to decide out how many
game markers of each color are likely to be in the bag. Demonstrate what you
mean by giving the bag a good shake to mix the markers thoroughly. Then
pull one out, show it to your students, return it to the bag, and shake the
bag thoroughly again. Then ask them if they think this one sample provides
enough information to determine how many red and blue markers there are
in the bag. Based on experiences in previous grades, and on common sense,
most will agree that more samples are needed.

Now explain that they will collect and record 5 samples for each day in January, including weekends and holidays. Ask them to determine how many
samples that would be in all and whether that seems like enough to make an
informed conclusion about how many of each marker are in the bag. (5 × 31
days = 155 samples in all) Then ask students to figure out how many samples
they will need to make today, based on how many days have passed so far
this month. (e.g., If today is January 4, they will need to collect and record 20
samples.)

Finally, have a few student volunteers draw the needed number of samples as
you record the data on the Sampling Record Sheet. Remind them not to look
in the bag and to return the markers to the bag each time and then give it a
good shake before drawing again.

Calendar Collector Sampling (cont.)

Once you have recorded their samples, ask students to share observations about the data and ideas about the probable contents of the bag. Can they identify which of the 8 possible combinations of red and blue there are in the bag with complete confidence? Why or why not?

....

Note *Throughout the month, students may be tempted to just open the bag and count how many of each color marker are inside. You will find it most effective to address this issue in a straightforward manner during this first workout. Explain that while it's tempting to peek, it will spoil all the fun. You'll need the cooperation of every student to make this a fair experiment.*

....

....

Week 2 Considering the Accumulated Data

Before you conduct the second Calendar Collector Workout, have a student helper make sure the record sheet is up to date. Then have another student or pair of students find the total number of red and blue samples that have been drawn so far and enter those numbers on the Sampling Data Chart overhead. This job needs to be done with great care and precision so that the totals are computed and entered correctly.

> **Alena** *Okay, I counted up the blues. It's 15.*
>
> **David** *I'll write 15 under blue on this record sheet. How many red?*
>
> **Alena** *Here, I have to add it up. Okay, 40 on the red.*

Calendar Collector Sampling (cont.)

David *So that means we've taken 55 markers so far.*

Alena *That sounds right. Today's the 11th and we take 5 a day, so 11 times 5 is 55.*

David *Do we have to fill in the graph too?*

Alena *No, he said to leave that part blank.*

Sampling Record Sheet				
Day	Marker Drawn	Daily Total		
		Blue	Red	

Day	Marker Drawn	Blue	Red
1		2	3
2		1	4
3		1	4
4		1	4
5		2	3
6		1	4
7		1	4
8		1	4
9		1	4
10		2	3
11		2	3
12			
13			
14			

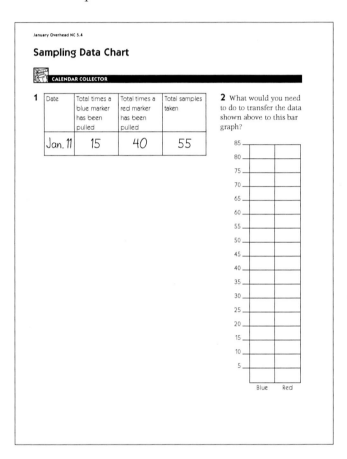

January Overhead NC 5.4

Sampling Data Chart

CALENDAR COLLECTOR

1

Date	Total times a blue marker has been pulled	Total times a red marker has been pulled	Total samples taken
Jan. 11	15	40	55

2 What would you need to do to transfer the data shown above to this bar graph?

Display the overhead and class record sheet at the beginning of the second workout and ask students to share observations and conjectures about the data. Then ask them to think about how they could transfer the information to the bar graph on the overhead. Discuss this in as much depth as necessary; many fourth-graders have had enough experience constructing bar graphs that you won't actually need to model the process, although you may need to call attention to the fact that each box on the graph represents more than one sample.

Next, have students complete Student Book page 49, Mid-Month Sampling Data. They will copy the data from the overhead onto their own chart, transfer it to a bar graph, record the possible combinations of red and blue markers that might be in the bag, select which of the 8 combinations they think is most likely at this point, and explain their selection.

Calendar Collector Sampling (cont.)

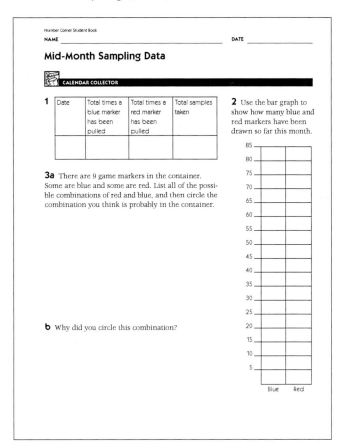

Number Corner Student Book

NAME _____ DATE _____

Mid-Month Sampling Data

CALENDAR COLLECTOR

1
Date	Total times a blue marker has been pulled	Total times a red marker has been pulled	Total samples taken

2 Use the bar graph to show how many blue and red markers have been drawn so far this month.

3a There are 9 game markers in the container. Some are blue and some are red. List all of the possible combinations of red and blue, and then circle the combination you think is probably in the container.

b Why did you circle this combination?

··

Week 3 Discussing the Likelihood of Drawing a Red Marker

Open your third Calendar Collector Workout by asking the following question: *We haven't yet taken the 5 samples for today. Based on the information we have collected so far, which color marker do you think we'll get on the first draw?*

Red has been in the lead throughout the month, so students may think it's almost a sure bet that the first marker out of the sack today will be red. Ask them to consider whether this prediction makes sense. This question gets at one of the big ideas in probability, which is that while the chances of getting red do not vary, this doesn't guarantee the outcome of a single sample. It's safe to say that if you take 10, 100, or 1000 samples from this bag of game markers, roughly $2/3$ will be red. In fact, the larger the sample size, the more likely that the experimental results will match the theoretical probability. But this doesn't make it any easier to say which color will come out of the bag *on any one draw.*

This is not an easy concept to grasp, and it is important to give students time to understand it through their own experiences. Give them time to discuss the question, draw a marker, and compare what happened to what they predicted would happen. Now have a volunteer take 4 more samples. Each time, have students predict what color marker they will draw before the sample is taken.

Calendar Collector Sampling (cont.)

When they have taken 5 samples, ask them if it's possible to predict the color of a single sample with complete confidence. (It's not.) Also ask if the results of the first, second, and third draws have any influence on the fourth and fifth. (They do not, since the game marker is returned to the bag each time.) Students will probably not reach a consensus about either question today, but their conversation will provide a great deal of information about their probability understandings and will prompt them to consider these questions through the end of the month.

Week 4 Drawing Conclusions about the Data

Before you conduct your last Calendar Collector Workout this month, compile the data collected so far on the Sampling Data Chart overhead, just as you did before the second workout. Display the overhead and have students enter the information on page 59 in their Student Books. They'll need to transfer the data to the bar graph (which they'll need to label in a way that will accommodate the data) and answer the questions based on the data and their own experiences this month.

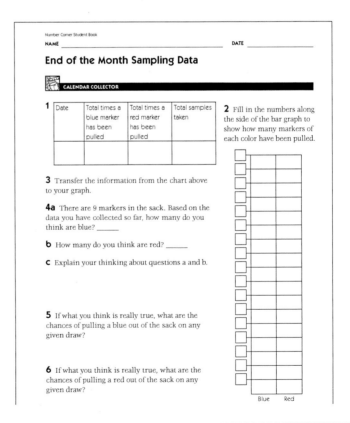

Note Unless your final Calendar Collector Workout happens to fall on the last day of the month, have a student helper continue to update the data collection each day. On January 31, or shortly thereafter, take a few minutes of class time to discuss the additional data and then reveal the contents of the bag.

January Computational Fluency

COMPUTATIONAL FLUENCY

Quick Facts

STUDENT BOOK

Overview

Students work on Quick Facts, practice sheets designed to help them master multiplication and division facts through 12. (A student is considered to have mastered a set of facts if she can complete them at a rate of 3 seconds per fact.) Quick Facts sheets are flexible, allowing students to choose their own sets of facts to practice each week. Students also take responsibility for mastering their facts by keeping track of their own progress. This routine will be featured during Computational Fluency Workouts over the next several months and can be extended beyond that time if necessary. A challenge game called Roll 5 is provided for those few students who have already mastered the facts through 12 × 12.

Frequency

One day per week

Skills & Concepts

★ fluently using multiplication facts through 12 × 12

★ developing efficient strategies for solving basic division facts

★ relating multiplication and division

You'll need

★ Quick Facts Worksheet (Overhead NC 5.1)

★ Quick Facts Tracking Sheet (Overhead NC 5.2)

★ Multiplication Facts Class Checklist (Blackline NC 5.5, 1 or 2 copies)

★ Quick Facts Worksheet (Blackline NC 5.6, 4 class sets)

★ Quick Facts Tracking Sheet (Number Corner Student Book, page 50)

★ Roll 5 (Number Corner Student Book, pages 51–54, optional)

★ 2 dice numbered 1–6 for each pair of students (optional)

__A Note about Timed Testing__ By limiting the time students have to complete a set of multiplication facts, teachers and students can see which facts come quickly and which don't. It is only through such timed checkups that teachers can see whether students have the speed that is an essential component of computational fluency. These timed exercises are formative assessments designed to help you decide how to tailor practice and support for each student. Toward this end, we have offered guidance on page 201 about assigning Support Activities for students who need more conceptual support and practice with specific groups of facts.

Timed checkups should be used for information purposes only, and students should not be graded on this work. We also do not advocate using timed drills for instructional purposes. Daily timed practice with random collections of problems is not productive to the development of computational fluency. Students typically

Computational Fluency Quick Facts (cont.)

continue to reinforce bad habits (e.g., counting on their fingers) when they are under pressure, and many develop a negative disposition toward mathematics because they cannot compete with their peers or can't work fast enough. Instead, students benefit from engaging practice with the facts they find challenging. We offer this practice in the form of Support Activities, which are described on page 214.

To read more about our approach to developing students' computational fluency, please see pages 14 and 15.

Introducing the Quick Facts Routine

Display the Quick Facts Worksheet overhead and explain that this month, students will start a new routine that will help them get faster and more confident with their multiplication and division facts. Give students a minute or two to examine the sheet and pair-share any observations and/or questions, and then call for whole group sharing.

Once students have had a chance to share their initial comments and questions, distribute copies of the Quick Facts Worksheet and explain that everyone will use the multiplier 2 today to get used to the routine. Explain that a multiplier is a number by which you multiply other numbers. Let them know that they will have up to 4 minutes to multiply the numbers in the boxes by the multiplier and record the products in the boxes. Model the recording process by writing your name on the sheet, filling in 2 as the multiplier, and then multiplying the top row of numbers by 2 with students' help. If necessary, remind them of the doubles strategy they practiced earlier in the year.

Explain that you'll keep track of time while they work. First, you'll write 0–1 on the whiteboard. Then, after they have been working for a minute, you'll write 1–2 on the board. After 2 minutes have passed, you'll record 2–3. After 3 minutes have passed, you'll write 3–4, and after 4 minutes have passed, you'll call time. As soon as they have finished the 40 multiplication facts, they're to turn their paper over, look up at the board, and record the last range of minutes you recorded. If, for instance, they turn their paper over, look up, and see 1–2, they're to write 1–2 on the back of their paper to indicate that they completed the work in 1–2 minutes. Let them know that everyone will remain silent for the entire 4 minutes, even if many of them finish before the time is up, so that they can concentrate without distraction. Then show them where to record the amount of time it took them to complete the facts.

Computational Fluency Quick Facts (cont.)

January Overhead NC 5.1

Quick Facts Worksheet

What's your multiplier?	How many minutes?	Number correct
2	1-2	

1 Multiply each number in the grid by your multiplier. Write each product in the box.

5	7	3	6	1	0	2	10
10	14	6	12	2	0	4	20
4	6	11	9	12	8	4	5
6	10	2	7	8	1	9	3
9	7	12	2	11	0	8	10
11	12	3	4	7	6	5	9

Reassure them that this exercise is designed to help them see which facts come quickly for them and which facts they need to practice. Assure them that they will not be graded on this work. Ask students to write their names and the date on their own papers, and enter the number 2 on the multiplier line. Then turn off the overhead, give the signal to start, and keep track of the time that has passed as students work. After 4 minutes have passed, ask them to stop, even if they're not finished. Remind students to transfer the number of minutes it took them to complete the 40 facts from the back of the sheet to the line at the top of the sheet.

Conclude the workout by demonstrating how to complete the division section at the bottom of the page, using your transparency to model the process. Read the instructions together, and then write 10 *different* products from the grid in the dividend boxes. Then record a 2 as the divisor on each line. After you have set up 10 division facts, work with students' help to enter the quotients along the top row, and then have students fill in their own sheets, entering the dividends in any order they choose.

2 Choose 10 *different* products from above (except 0) and record them in the 10 boxes below. Then divide each by your multiplier.

$$2\overline{)10} \;\; 2\overline{)4} \;\; 2\overline{)8} \;\; 2\overline{)12} \;\; 2\overline{)6}$$

quotients: 5, 2, 4, 6, 3

$$2\overline{)16} \;\; 2\overline{)14} \;\; 2\overline{)18} \;\; 2\overline{)20} \;\; 2\overline{)24}$$

quotients: 8, 7, 9, 10, 12

As students finish, collect their papers and explain that you'll return them the following week. Sometime before the next Computational Fluency Workout, you'll need to look over students' work and record the number they got

Computational Fluency Quick Facts (cont.)

correct at the top of the page. You can also use the Multiplication Facts Class Checklist throughout the month to keep track of which students have mastered each group of facts.

Continuing through the Month with Quick Facts

At the beginning of each workout, return students' scored Quick Facts Worksheets from the previous week. Model on the overhead how they should record their multiplier, date, time, and number correct on the Quick Facts Tracking Sheet. If they got 38 or more correct in 1–2 minutes, they'll pick a new multiplier to work with today. If they got fewer than 38 correct and/or it took them longer than 2 minutes to complete the facts, they'll need to work with the same multiplier this week.

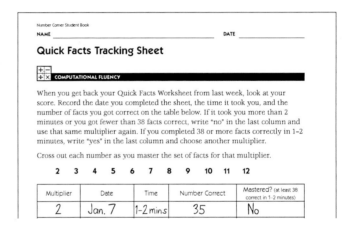

When students get to pick a new multiplier, encourage them to choose carefully, thinking about which facts they really need to work on. They don't necessarily need to do them in order, and we find that students are much more motivated to memorize their facts when they set their own targets. They'll need to work with each multiplier until they can complete at least 38 facts correctly in no more than 2 minutes.

Once the Quick Facts routine is firmly in place, you might give students about 5 minutes to practice with their multiplier before starting the worksheet. There are many quick and simple ways to do this, including the following:

• Have students write their own set of flashcards on the spot and then "test" each other.

• Give each pair of students 2 dice numbered 1–6. Have them announce their multipliers to each other and then take turns rolling the 2 dice, adding the 2 numbers, and multiplying the sum by their multiplier.

• Have students list the facts for their multiplier several times on a piece of paper.

• If your classroom is equipped with computers, students can play a quick multiplication practice game electronically.

Computational Fluency Quick Facts (cont.)

CHALLENGE

If you find that some of your students know all their facts, give them alternate tasks during this workout for the next couple of months. They might serve as tutors for students who are having a difficult time, or they might work independently on some of the problems from the Problem Solving Workout they haven't had time to complete. Another option is to have them play Roll 5, a game that uses all 4 operations and is nearly unlimited in terms of challenge level. The instructions and several copies of the record sheet for this game can be found on pages 51–54 in the Number Corner Student Book.

Number Corner Student Book

NAME _____ DATE _____

Roll 5

COMPUTATIONAL FLUENCY

You and your partner will need

★ Roll 5 Instructions (Number Corner Student Book, page 51)

★ Roll 5 Record Sheet (Number Corner Student Book, pages 52–54)

★ 5 dice (1 numbered 0–5, 2 numbered 1–6, and 2 numbered 4–9)

★ calculators

★ scratch paper

Instructions for Roll 5

1 Use any method you want to decide which player will go first.

2 Roll any two dice and then multiply the two numbers on the dice. The product is your target number. Record it on your side of the record sheet.

3 Then roll all 5 dice and write these numbers on your side of the sheet.

4 Add, subtract, multiply, or divide any combination of the 5 numbers you just rolled to get to your target number. (You don't have to use all 5 of the numbers you rolled, but use as many as you can because you score a point for each.) If you can't find any way to get to your target number with the 5 numbers you rolled, roll two of the

dice and multiply the numbers to get a different target number.

5 With your partner, double-check your equation to make sure it works. Be sure to use parentheses to show how you combined the numbers to get to your target.

6 Count how many numbers you used. You get a point for each number. Record the points in the space provided.

7 Take turns until you have each gone 4 times. Then add up your points. The player with the most points wins.

Number Corner Student Book

NAME _____ DATE _____

Roll 5 Record Sheet page 1 of 3

COMPUTATIONAL FLUENCY

Player 1 _____   Player 2 _____

		Target Number						Target Number	
Round 1		5 Numbers Rolled						5 Numbers Rolled		
		My Equation _____						My Equation _____		
		Points scored this round _____						Points scored this round _____		

Round 1:
- Target Number / 5 Numbers Rolled / My Equation _____ / Points scored this round _____
- (Player 2 same)

Round 2:
- Target Number / 5 Numbers Rolled / My Equation _____ / Points scored this round _____

Round 3:
- Target Number / 5 Numbers Rolled / My Equation _____ / Points scored this round _____

Round 4:
- Target Number / 5 Numbers Rolled / My Equation _____ / Points scored this round _____

Total: Player 1's Total Score _____   Player 2's Total Score _____

SUPPORT

We want all fourth graders to be fluent with their multiplication facts by the end of the school year, and some students will not reach this goal without considerable support. If, after the first month of Quick Facts, you still have students working with 2's or 3's, and struggling to do so, you may want to have them play some of the support games listed after this month's Number Corner Checkup with a paraprofessional, resource room teacher, or parent.

January Problem Solving

PROBLEM SOLVING

STUDENT BOOK

TECHNOLOGY CONNECTION

Time, Perimeter, Patterns & Money

Overview

The Problem Solving Workouts this month take the form of four pages in the Student Book. With four problems on each sheet, these pages give students an opportunity to find the perimeter and area of rectangles, make computations with money, find the missing elements in patterned sequences of numbers, calculate elapsed time, and solve story problems. Each week, students complete the problems that interest them and then share their solutions and strategies for some of the problems as a class.

Frequency

One day per week

Skills & Concepts

★ using different models of division to solve problems

★ multiplying and dividing 2- and 3-digit numbers by 1-digit numbers

★ adding and subtracting decimals to hundredths using money amounts

★ extending number patterns that grow by common differences

★ developing strategies for finding the perimeter and area of rectangles

★ determining elapsed time

★ selecting methods and tools appropriate to a particular context for operations with whole numbers

★ solving multi-step story problems using a variety of efficient paper/pencil and mental strategies

You'll need

★ January Problem Solving Sheets 1–4 (Overheads NC 5.3 and 5.5–5.7)

★ January Problem Solving Sheets 1–4 (Number Corner Student Book, pages 46, 55, 56 and 60)

★ plastic or real coins and paper bills (Use Blackline NC 1.13 to make paper bills if needed.)

★ half-class set of student clocks

★ calculators

★ overhead pens and a few blank overhead transparencies

★ piece of paper to mask parts of the overhead when necessary

Problem Solving Time, Perimeter, Patterns & Money (cont.)

Three of the four Problem Solving sheets this month feature 4 problems in a variety of contexts and of varying levels of difficulty. On these pages, we recommend that you have students choose the problems they want to work on, based on their interests and ability levels. Afterwards, have students share solutions and strategies, focusing the discussion on problems that were completed by most students or that proved particularly challenging for those who attempted them.

On the second sheet, however, have students complete all of the problems individually or in pairs. Students will find the area and perimeter of 3 rectangles that have the same area but different perimeters. The fourth item on the sheets asks students to fill in a chart of their findings and to record their observations. This sheet provides another opportunity to consider the difference between perimeter and area and may elicit some lively discussion about of how it is possible for 3 rectangles with the same area to each have a different perimeter.

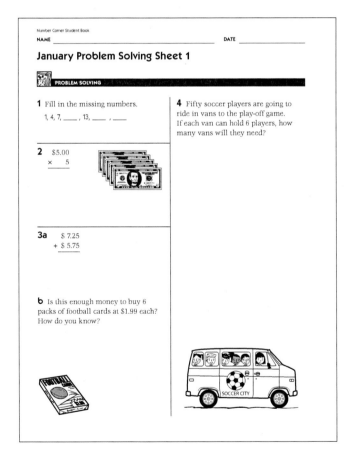

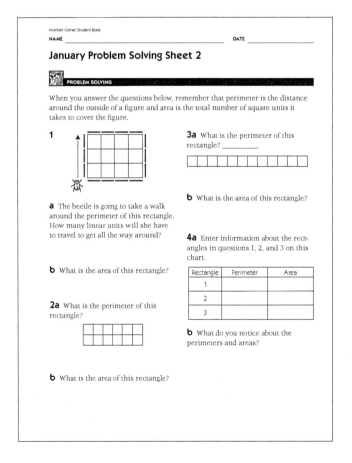

Problem Solving Time, Perimeter, Patterns & Money (cont.)

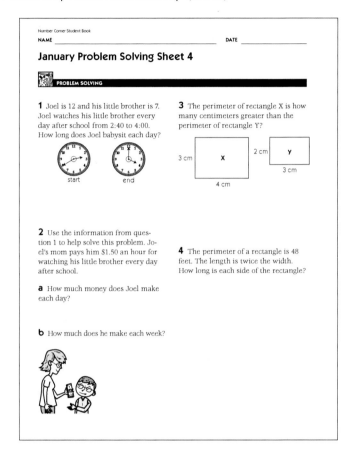

Number Corner Student Book
NAME _____   DATE _____

January Problem Solving Sheet 3

PROBLEM SOLVING

1 The team started their basketball game at 1:00. The clock shows the time when the game was over. How long did the game last? _____

2a Fill in the blanks to show the two numbers that you think come next in this number pattern.

8, 11, 10, 13, 12, 15, 14, _____, _____

b Explain your answer.

3a What is the perimeter of this rectangle? _____

9 feet

6 feet

b Write a number sentence to show how you figured it out.

4 Alec built a rectangular pen for his rabbit. The perimeter of the pen is 40 feet and one of the sides is 5 feet. How long are the other three sides?

Number Corner Student Book
NAME _____   DATE _____

January Problem Solving Sheet 4

PROBLEM SOLVING

1 Joel is 12 and his little brother is 7. Joel watches his little brother every day after school from 2:40 to 4:00. How long does Joel babysit each day?

start   end

2 Use the information from question 1 to help solve this problem. Joel's mom pays him $1.50 an hour for watching his little brother every day after school.

a How much money does Joel make each day?

b How much does he make each week?

3 The perimeter of rectangle X is how many centimeters greater than the perimeter of rectangle Y?

3 cm   X   2 cm   Y
         4 cm   3 cm

4 The perimeter of a rectangle is 48 feet. The length is twice the width. How long is each side of the rectangle?

Time-Saving Reminders

- Depending on the needs and skills of your class, you may find that you want to do Problem Solving Workouts twice a week and omit one of the other workouts, such as Computational Fluency or the Number Line. All the workouts have their merits, but you may want and need to place a heavier stress on the skills and concepts featured on this month's Problem Solving sheets.

- Rather than trying to cover everything in one workout, you can use your Number Corner period to present the problems and get students started. Assign some or all of the problems they didn't complete as homework, and take some time the following day to have students discuss their strategies and solutions, at least in pairs, if not as a whole group.

- If you usually have students do seatwork as they come in each morning, you might assign a Problem Solving sheet at the beginning of the week and have students complete the four problems over 2 or 3 days. This will allow you to spend the first few minutes of your Problem Solving Workout having students meet in pairs to discuss their strategies and solutions, and the rest of the workout doing whole-class sharing.

- In order to facilitate whole-group sharing, make 2–3 extra copies of the Problem Solving overheads and cut them apart. Distribute these quarter-sheets to students so they can copy their work directly onto the slips to share during class discussion.

January Number Line

NUMBER LINE

Multiples of 7 & Games with Numbers to 10,000

TECHNOLOGY CONNECTION

Overview

Student helpers continue to add a number to the Number Line for each day of school. Students locate the multiples of 7, in addition to the other multiples they have been locating in months past. Students also play two games on the open number line in which they read, order, round, and compare 3- and 4-digit numbers.

Frequency

Update the Number Line each day and do a whole-group workout once a week.

Skills & Concepts

★ reading, ordering, identifying, and comparing the place value of digits in whole numbers

★ rounding 3- and 4-digit whole numbers to the nearest thousand

★ exploring factors of whole numbers through 100

You'll need

★ Open Number Line (Overhead NC 3.9)

★ Open Number Line (Blackline NC 4.9, class set, optional)

★ number line

★ 4 dice, 2 marked 1–6 and 2 marked 4–9

★ calculators

★ pointer (such as a yard or meter stick)

★ blank overhead transparency

★ overhead pens in black, red, and blue

★ colored pencils in red and blue (optional)

★ a few small slips of scratch paper

Week 1 Updating the Number Line & Identifying Multiples of 7

During the first workout this month, have students update and discuss the Number Line. Ask them to think about whether the next number will be a multiple of 2, 3, 4, 5, and/or 6. How do they know? While many students will use the pattern of markings on the number line, encourage them to think of other ways to demonstrate the fact that the number is a multiple of 2, 3, 4, 5, and/or 6.

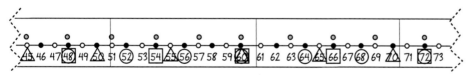

• Multiples of 2   ◦ Multiples of 3   ◯ Multiples of 4   △ Multiples of 5   ☐ Multiples of 6

Number Line Multiples of 7 & Games with Numbers to 10,000 (cont.)

Madelyn *It's going to be 74 days. Yesterday was day 73, so we're going to write 74 on the line. And we'll need to color in the dot because 74 is a multiple of 2.*

Teacher *How do you know?*

Madelyn *You can just look at the pattern on the number line. The dot over the 72 is colored in, so the one over the 74 will be too.*

Teacher *Can you think of any other way to explain the fact that 74 is a multiple of 2?*

Students *74 is an even number. All even numbers are multiples of 2. You can divide 74 by 2. It's 37 plus 37. If you count by 2's, you'll land on 74.*

Teacher *Is 74 a multiple of 3, 4, 5, or 6?*

Students *It's not a multiple of 3 because we just marked 72 as a multiple of 3. The next multiple of 3 won't come until 75. I think maybe 74 is a multiple of 4 because it ends with a 4 You can see by the pattern on the line that it's not. The next multiple of 4 won't be until 76.*

Teacher *Is there any way to determine whether or not 74 is a multiple of 4 without looking at the pattern on the line? Share your thinking with a partner. See if you can come up with a different way.*

Students *We could count by 4's and see if we land on 74, but that would take so long! We could start with 40 and then count by 4's. We know for sure 40 is a multiple of 4. Or we could use a calculator and see what happens if we divide 74 by 4. It won't come out even, I bet, because 70 divided by 4 is weird. Also, we just marked 72 as a multiple of 4.*

Such discussions provide an opportunity for students to make generalizations about the multiples of 2, 3, 4, 5, and 6, and to share the strategies they use to determine whether or not a number is divisible by another number.

After students have had a chance to update the number line, ask them to identify the multiples of 7, and invite them to make observations and conjectures about the patterns they see now.

Number Line Multiples of 7 & Games with Numbers to 10,000 (cont.)

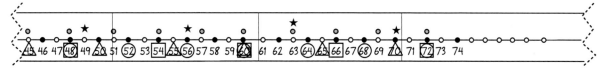

• Multiples of 2   ∘ Multiples of 3   ◯ Multiples of 4   △ Multiples of 5   ☐ Multiples of 6   ★ Multiples of 7

Students *We finally got to mark the 7. I thought we'd never get there! Here's something! The multiples of 7 go odd, even, odd, even – see? They're 7, 14, 21, 28, 35, 42...*

And every third one is also a multiple of 3, because it's 21, 42, then 63. Wow! If you keep going on the pattern of 7's, the next one will be 77, and after that, 84. That's weird, because 84 doesn't sound like a number you could divide by 7.

Let's try it and see!

Week 2 Playing What's My Number?

Open the second workout by displaying the Open Number Line overhead. As students watch, use an erasable black marker to label the leftmost dot 0 and the rightmost dot 10,000.

Next, ask students to share suggestions for how to label the 9 marks between the 0 and the 10,000. This question may spark some interesting discussion, but students will likely agree after some discussion that because there are 9 evenly spaced marks, each should be labeled as a multiple of 1000. After you have labeled all the points as shown below, place a blank transparency over the sheet to prevent the ink from smearing and introduce the game of What's My Number?.

Note *You may want to give each student a copy of the Open Number Line blackline so they can record the guesses during the game.*

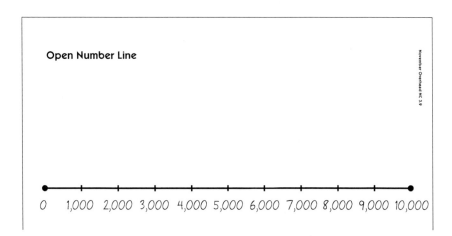

Number Line Multiples of 7 & Games with Numbers to 10,000 (cont.)

Explain that in today's game, you will write a random number between 0 and 10,000 on a slip of paper, which is kept secret from the students. The students will play in two teams, taking turns to guess your number. Each time they make a guess, you'll record it where it belongs along the number line. You'll record guesses that are *less than your number in red* and guesses that are *greater than your number in blue*. (It may help to make a note about the color-coding at the whiteboard for students' reference.)

Now divide the class into two teams and have them take turns guessing your number. With each new guess, the range of possibilities is narrowed dramatically, allowing students to quickly "zero in" on your number. Remember to mark numbers higher than your number in blue and numbers lower than your number in red. (In the black-and-white visual below, higher numbers are shown above the line, and lower numbers are shown below the line.)

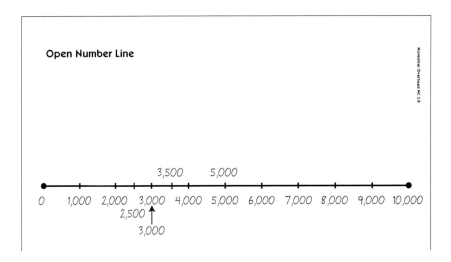

Rafael Well, if 3000 is lower and 3500 is higher, we know her number has to be between 3000 and 3500. So let's pick 3200.

This game provides opportunities for reading, ordering, and comparing 4-digit numbers, and also for talking about the concept of *range* (the difference between the greatest and the least number in a set). At first, some students will probably make guesses that are outside the identified range. It will help everyone if you have students explain their guesses each time.

Have the teams continue taking turns until someone names the exact number. This process may unfold with surprising speed, especially after students understand how it works. Once your number has been identified, show students the slip of paper on which you recorded it, and play the game again if time allows. After playing a round or two, turn the game over to the class, allowing the student who identified the number exactly to pick the next number and record the guesses on the line.

Number Line Multiples of 7 & Games with Numbers to 10,000 (cont.)

Week 3 Round & Add to the Nearest Thousand

The third workout returns to the familiar game of Round and Add, played to the nearest thousand this month. As before, the objective of Round and Add is two-fold: 1) to get the highest score and 2) to make an accurate estimate about which team is going to win the game based on adding the team's rounded numbers. If you've erased your Open Number Line transparency, relabel the multiples of 1000 before playing the game.

Explain to the class that you're going to play a new version of Round and Add today, this time working with 3- and 4-digit numbers and rounding to the nearest 1000. Begin the game by asking one of the students to roll the dice for you. Record the four numbers at the board and share your thinking about how to arrange these digits to form a number most advantageous to you. As you do, remind students that to round a 4-digit number to the nearest thousand, they need to look at the digits in the hundreds place. If the digit indicates a number less than 500, the 4-digit number rounds down; if it's 500 or more, the number rounds up. Once you've made a decision, record the number where it belongs on the Open Number Line and then circle the multiple of 1000 to which it rounds. Mark your results in red and the class's results in blue so that you can tell the difference as the game proceeds.

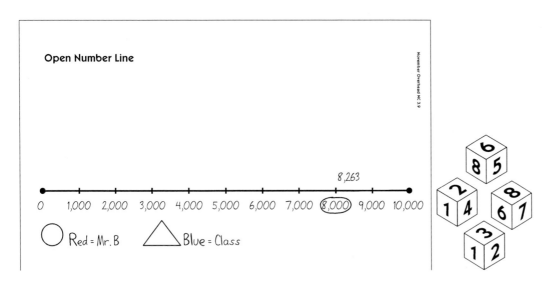

Now have a volunteer roll for the class and write the 4 digits on the whiteboard. Ask students to talk in small groups about how they want to arrange the 4 digits. Remind them that they'll need to arrange the digits to form a number that rounds to a multiple different from the multiple you've just claimed. Then have them discuss their options as a class. After a minute or two, students will agree on the most advantageous number, which you'll need to mark on the number line and then circle the multiple to which it rounds.

Continue taking turns until all the multiples have been claimed by one team or the other. If either you or the class rolls 4 digits that cannot be arranged to

Number Line Multiples of 7 & Games with Numbers to 10,000 (cont.)

form a number that rounds to an unclaimed multiple of 1000, the turn is lost. Either team can decide to use just 3 of the number cubes whenever the players decide they want to claim the 0.

After all the multiples on the line have been circled, ask students to estimate which team will have the higher score. Then have students find the actual scores (using efficient mental strategies, paper/pencil methods, or calculators). The team with the higher actual score wins.

Week 4 Games on the Open Number Line

In the last Number Line Workout of the month, play Round and Add and/or several rounds of What's My Number? If you decide to play Round and Add, you might consider introducing a slightly different version of the game in which the team that is able to get its actual and rounded totals *to match most closely wins.*

This twist on the now-familiar game encourages students to pay very close attention to how they arrange the 4 digits they roll each time. Here's an example: 4, 2, 1, and 9 can be arranged to form a variety of 4-digit numbers, including 9,421 and 9,124. In this version of the game, it is more advantageous to form 9,124. Both numbers round to 9,000, but 9,124 is considerably closer to 9,000 than is 9,421. This is an advantage when the goal is to have the total of the rounded numbers match the total of the actual numbers as closely as possible.

January Assessment

ASSESSMENT

Number Corner Checkup 2

Overview

In place of regular workouts, students spend two Number Corner periods completing a four-page skills checkup. The teacher may use a class checklist to record assessment results and get an overview of students' strengths, as well as the areas in which they'll need more work.

Timing

Last week of January or first week of February

Skills & Concepts

★ demonstrating fluency with multiplication facts through 10 × 10

★ carrying out simple unit conversions in the U.S. customary system

★ finding the area and perimeter of a rectangle

★ determining elapsed time in minutes

★ rounding to the nearest 100 and recognizing which place will be the most helpful in estimating an answer

★ adding and subtracting 2- and 3-digit numbers with regrouping

★ multiplying and dividing a 2-digit number by a 1-digit number

★ recognizing equivalent forms of common fractions and decimals to hundredths

★ demonstrating an understanding of multiplication and division

You'll need

★ Number Corner Checkup 2, pages 1–4 (Blacklines NC A 5.1–5.4)

★ Number Corner Checkup 2 Class Checklist, pages 1 and 2 (Blacklines NC A 5.5 and 5.6, 2 or 3 copies as needed, optional)

★ half-class set of student clocks (optional)

★ one-third class set of base ten pieces (optional, Use Blackline NC 1.9 to make your own if needed.)

★ paper bills (optional, Use Blackline NC 1.13 to make your own if needed.)

★ one-third class set of money value pieces (optional, Use Blackline NC 1.10–1.12 to make your own if needed.)

Assessment Number Corner Checkup 2 (cont.)

Day 1 Number Corner Checkup 2, Pages 1 & 2

We recommend that you have students complete the first two pages of the Number Corner Checkup during one of your regular Number Corner periods at the end of January or very early in February. They can then complete pages 3 and 4 the following day, again during your regular Number Corner period.

The first page is a set of 40 multiplication facts. Conduct this page as a timed test, giving students 2 minutes to complete as many of the 40 facts as they can. Then give students as much time as they need to complete the second page.

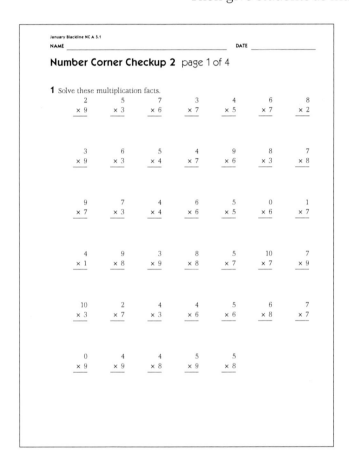

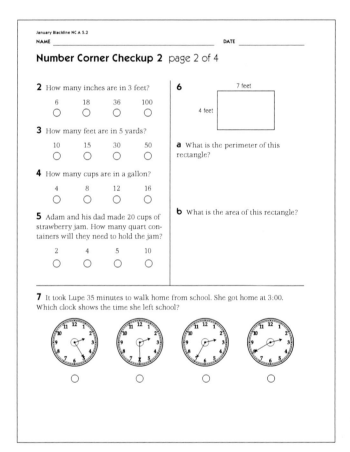

It may be interesting for both you and the students to contrast the number of facts they completed correctly on the first page this time to the number they were able to complete correctly at the end of October. If many students are still developing fluency with multiplication facts, stress that this is just a check-in designed to help them (and you) see what they still need to work on. If most of your students are already quite fluent with their multiplication facts by now, however, you might consider eliminating this page of the checkup.

Assessment Number Corner Checkup 2 (cont.)

....

Day 2 Number Corner Checkup 2, Pages 3 & 4

The day after they have completed the first two pages, give students a full Number Corner period to complete the last two pages of the checkup. Make manipulatives available for those who want to use them.

The second part of this month's Number Corner Checkup is designed to provide you with windows into students' current computation and estimation skills and strategies. You may find it interesting to compare students' methods on this checkup to their work on similar items on the October Checkup.

You will get a much more accurate picture of children's true understandings if you require all of them to explain their thinking and their notation. If students use a traditional or invented algorithm, have them explain it using words, numbers, and sketches. In looking over their work, you may find that although some students can apply an algorithm to produce a correct answer, their responses do not demonstrate an understanding of the place values involved, as shown in the two samples below.

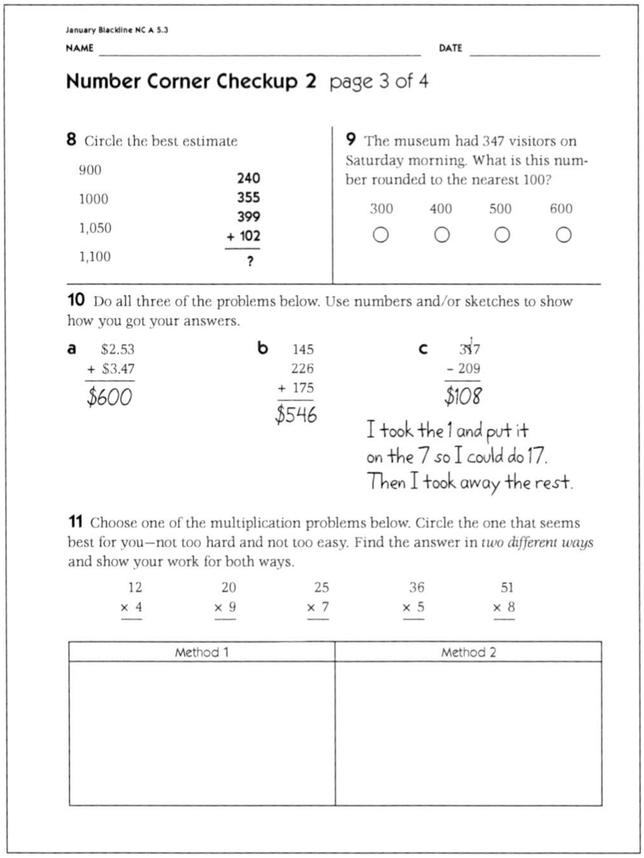

January Blackline NC A 5.3

NAME _____ DATE _____

Number Corner Checkup 2 page 3 of 4

8 Circle the best estimate

900
1000
1,050
1,100

240
355
399
+ 102
?

9 The museum had 347 visitors on Saturday morning. What is this number rounded to the nearest 100?

300   400   500   600
○   ○   ○   ○

10 Do all three of the problems below. Use numbers and/or sketches to show how you got your answers.

a $2.53
     + $3.47
     $600

b   145
      226
    + 175
     $546

c   3⁴7
      − 209
      $108

I took the 1 and put it on the 7 so I could do 17. Then I took away the rest.

11 Choose one of the multiplication problems below. Circle the one that seems best for you—not too hard and not too easy. Find the answer in *two different ways* and show your work for both ways.

12   20   25   36   51
× 4   × 9   × 7   × 5   × 8

Method 1	Method 2

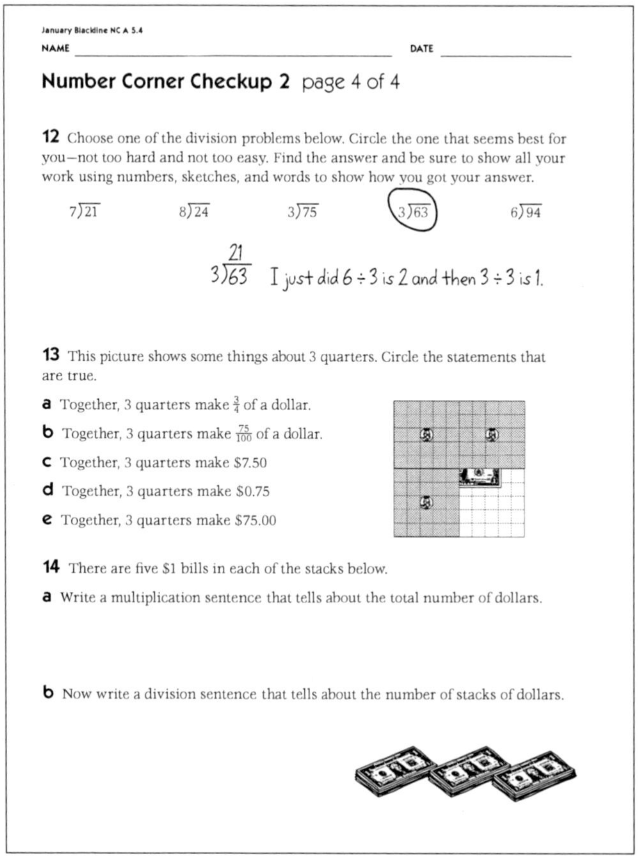

January Blackline NC A 5.4

NAME _____ DATE _____

Number Corner Checkup 2 page 4 of 4

12 Choose one of the division problems below. Circle the one that seems best for you—not too hard and not too easy. Find the answer and be sure to show all your work using numbers, sketches, and words to show how you got your answer.

7)21   8)24   3)75   ⟮3)63⟯   6)94

$$\frac{21}{3)63}$$ I just did 6 ÷ 3 is 2 and then 3 ÷ 3 is 1.

13 This picture shows some things about 3 quarters. Circle the statements that are true.

a Together, 3 quarters make $\frac{3}{4}$ of a dollar.

b Together, 3 quarters make $\frac{75}{100}$ of a dollar.

c Together, 3 quarters make $7.50

d Together, 3 quarters make $0.75

e Together, 3 quarters make $75.00

14 There are five $1 bills in each of the stacks below.

a Write a multiplication sentence that tells about the total number of dollars.

b Now write a division sentence that tells about the number of stacks of dollars.

Assessment Number Corner Checkup 2 (cont.)

 SUPPORT

Support Activities

Students' work on the checkup may indicate that some need continued support with specific skills and concepts. You can have select students use specific support activities with a resource room teacher, instructional assistant, and/or parent to improve specific skills and strengthen conceptual understandings. You may find the activities listed below particularly helpful with skills featured on this checkup.

SUPPORT ACTIVITIES		
Activity	**Name**	**Topic**
Activity 10	An Hour or Bust	telling time and calculating elapsed time
Activity 11	Get Me to the Bus on Time	telling time and calculating elapsed time
Activity 12	Spinning Around Multiplication	strategies for multiplication facts up to 6 x 6
Activity 13	Array Challenge	multiplication facts to 8 x 9 with the array model
Activity 14	Multiplication Challenge	multiplication facts to 8 x 8 with a variety of models
Activity 15	Spinning for Arrays	multiplication facts to 8 x 10 with the array model
Activity 16	Product Bingo	practice of multiplication facts to 9 x 9
Activity 17	What's Missing? Bingo	practice of multiplication and division facts to 9 x 6

January Answer Keys

ANSWER KEY

Assessment Blacklines

Blacklines NC A 5.1–5.4, Number Corner Checkup 2

1 18, 15, 42, 21, 20, 42, 16
27, 18, 20, 28, 54, 24, 56
63, 21, 16, 36, 25, 0, 7
4, 72, 27, 64, 35, 70, 63
30, 14, 12, 24, 30, 48, 49
0, 36, 32, 45, 40

2 36 inches in 3 feet

3 15 feet in 5 yards

4 16 cups per gallon

5 5 quart containers to hold 20 cups of jam

6 **a** 22 feet

   b 28 square feet

7 First choice

8 1,100

9 300

10 a $6.00
Students' work will vary widely. Examples:
example 1:

example 2:

$$\begin{array}{r} \overset{1}{}\overset{1}{\$2.}53 \\ + \$3.47 \\ \hline \$6.00 \end{array}$$

   b 546
Students' work will vary widely. Examples:
example 1:

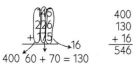

$$\begin{array}{r} 400 \\ 130 \\ + 16 \\ \hline 546 \end{array}$$

$400 \quad 60 + 70 = 130$

10 b example 2:

$$\begin{array}{r} 145 \\ 226 \\ + 175 \end{array} \searrow \begin{array}{r} 145 \\ + 175 \\ \hline 320 \end{array} \quad \begin{array}{r} 226 \\ + 320 \\ \hline 546 \end{array}$$

   c 108
Students' work will vary widely. Examples:
example 1:

$$\begin{array}{r} 317 + 1 = 318 \\ -209 + 1 = 210 \end{array} \quad \begin{array}{r} 318 \\ -210 \\ \hline 108 \end{array}$$

example 2:

$$\begin{array}{r} 317 \\ -209 \end{array} \quad \begin{array}{l} 209 + \boxed{100} = 309 \\ 309 + \boxed{8} = 317 \\ 100 + 8 = 108 \end{array}$$

11 $12 \times 4 = 48$, $20 \times 9 = 180$, $25 \times 7 = 175$,
$36 \times 5 = 180$, $51 \times 8 = 408$
Students' choice of problem and solution methods
will vary.

12 $21 \div 7 = 3$, $24 \div 8 = 3$, $75 \div 3 = 25$, $63 \div 3 = 21$,
$94 \div 6 = 15\ R4$
Students' choice of problem and solution methods
will vary.

13 a, b, and d are true (c and e are false)

14 a $5 \times 3 = 15$ ($5 per stack $\times$ 3 stacks = $15)
Students may or may not label each element in
their equations this way.

   b $15 \div 5 = 3$ ($15 $\div$ $5 per stack = 3 stacks)
Students may or may not label each element in
their equations this way.

Number Corner Student Book

page 46, January Problem Solving Sheet 1

1 10, 16, 19 (add 3 each time)

2 $25

3 a $13

ANSWER KEY

Number Corner Student Book (cont.)

page 46, January Problem Solving Sheet 1 (cont.)

3 b Yes, $13 is enough money to buy 6 packs of football cards at $1.99 each.

Students' explanations will vary. Example:
I know because if each pack was $2, it would be $12 altogether. But they're only $1.99 so it will be less than $12 altogether, and we have $13.

4 9 vans are needed.

Students' work will vary. Example:

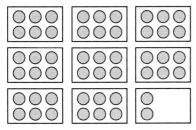

8 × 6 = 48, so 48 kids fill 8 vans. Then you need another whole van to take the last two kids.

pages 47 and 48, Night & Day

1 a 2:20 a.m.
  b 3:30 a.m.
  c 4:40 a.m.
  d 5:50 a.m.
  e 7:00 a.m.
  f 8:20 a.m.
  g 9:40 a.m.
  h 11:00 a.m.

2 1 hour and 10 minutes

3 1 hour and 20 minutes

4 a While most students will predict that the time will be 3:00 p.m. on the 13th, others may suggest different, but equally plausible, possibilities. If so, make sure that their explanations in part b make sense.

3 p.m.

4 b Students' explanations will vary. Example:
For 7 days, it went up by an hour and 10 minutes. Then it switched to an hour and 20 minutes. I think it will do that for 7 more days, until the 14th. So the 11th is 12:20 a.m., the 12th is 1:40 p.m., and then the 13th will be 3:00 p.m.

5 Students will describe different patterns and make different predictions. Example:
It goes up 1 hour and 10 minutes for 7 days. Then it goes up 1 hour and 20 minutes. I think it will do that for 7 days. Then maybe it will go up 1 hour and 30 minutes. It will go up by 10 more minutes every 7 days.

page 49, Mid-Month Sampling Data

1 Students' data will vary depending upon the date they complete this page and upon the number of red and blue markers pulled in your classroom.

2 Students' bar graphs will vary depending on your class data. Be sure they have filled in the bar graph to reflect your class results accurately.

3 a 1 red, 8 blue
  2 red, 7 blue
  3 red, 6 blue
  4 red, 5 blue
  5 red, 4 blue
  6 red, 3 blue
  7 red, 2 blue
  8 red, 1 blue
  Students will circle different collections of red and blue markers based on your class data and their understandings of sampling.

  b Students' explanations will vary.

page 55, January Problem Solving Sheet 2

1 a 14 linear units
  b 12 square units

2 a 16 linear units
  b 12 square units

3 a 26 linear units
  b 12 square units

ANSWER KEY

Number Corner Student Book (cont.)

page 55, January Problem Solving Sheet 2 (cont.)

4 a

Rectangle	Perimeter	Area
1	14 linear units	12 square units
2	16 linear units	12 square units
3	26 linear units	12 square units

b Students' observations will vary. Example:
I notice that the perimeters are different, but all the areas are the same.

page 56, January Problem Solving Sheet 3

1 2 hours, 25 minutes

2 a 17, 16

b Students' explanations will vary. Example:
It adds 3 and then subtracts 1 over and over. So 14 plus 3 is 17, and 17 – 1 = 16.

3 a 30 feet

b Students' number sentences will vary. Examples:
example 1: $9 + 9 + 6 + 6 = 18 + 12 = 30$
example 2: $2 \times (9 + 6) = 2 \times 15 = 30$

4 5 feet, 15 feet, and 15 feet
Students' strategies will vary. Examples:
example 1: *One other side has to be 5 feet, because it is a rectangle. So 40 – 10 = 30 feet for the other 2 sides. The other 2 sides have to be equal, so they are both 15 feet long.*
example 2:

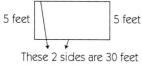

These 2 sides are 30 feet altogether. So each one has to be 15 feet.

pages 57 and 58, The Twins' School Day

1 8:20 a.m., 10:00 a.m., 11:50 a.m., 1:40 p.m., 3:30 p.m.

2 3 hours and 30 minutes or 3 and a half hours

3 3 hours and 40 minutes

4 7 hours

5 4:45 p.m.

6 50 minutes

7 a 3:45 p.m.

b Students' explanations will vary. Example:
The bus comes at 00, 15, 30, and 45 minutes. Since it's after 3:30, they missed the 3:30 bus and will have to get the 3:45 bus.

page 59, End of the Month Sampling Data

1 Students' data will vary depending upon the date they complete this page and upon the number of red and blue markers pulled in your classroom.

2 Students will need to fill in the numbers along the vertical axis of the bar graph in equal intervals that will accommodate the data.

3 Students' bar graphs will vary depending on your class data. Be sure they have filled in the bar graph to reflect your class results accurately.

4 a Students' responses will vary.

b Students' responses will vary.

c Students' explanations will vary.

5 Students' responses will vary. They should express the chances of pulling a blue marker as a fraction of the total number of markers. (e.g., $^3/_9$ or $^1/_3$)

6 Students' responses will vary. They should express the chances of pulling a red marker as a fraction of the total number of markers. (e.g., $^6/_9$ or $^2/_3$)

page 60, January Problem Solving Sheet 4

1 1 hour and 20 minutes

2 a $2

b $10

3 4 cm

4 8 feet, 8 feet, 16 feet, 16 feet
Students' strategies will vary. Example:

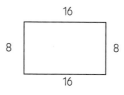

$10 + 10 + 20 + 20 = 60$ (too much)
$9 + 9 + 18 + 18 = 18 + 36 = 54$ (too much)
$8 + 8 + 16 + 16 = 48!$

Number Line

● Multiples of 2 ○ Multiples of 3 ○ Multiples of 4 △ Multiples of 5 ☐ Multiples of 6 ★ Multiples of 7

● Multiples of 2 ○ Multiples of 3 ○ Multiples of 4 △ Multiples of 5 ☐ Multiples of 6 ★ Multiples of 7

0 1 2 3 4 5 6 7 8 9 10 11 12 13 14 15 16 17 18 19 20 21 22 23 24 25 26 27 28 29 30 31 32 33 34 35 36 37 38 39 40 41 42 43 44 45 46 47 48 49 50 51 52 53 54 55 56 57 58 59 60

Calendar Collector

Roll & Multiply Record Sheet						
Day	Products					Number of Odd Products	Number of Even Products

Day		Prod	ucts			Number of Odd Products	Number of Even Products
1	42	20	20	30	63	1	4
2	40	64	72	45	36	1	4
3	20	48	28	54	54	0	5
4	32	16	81	54	42	3	2
5	54	48	25	81	35	3	2
6	48	35	64	20	72	1	4
7	48	72	49	63	35	3	2
8	72	45	63	54	32	2	3
9	36	25	25	49	42	3	2
10	72	30	56	63	20	1	4
11	40	20	49	20	36	1	4
12	30	20	45	81	45	3	2
13	40	24	81	32	40	1	4
14	45	42	25	56	32	2	3
15	56	28	48	30	36	0	5
16							

Calendar Grid

❄ February

Sunday	Monday	Tuesday	Wednesday	Thursday	Friday	Saturday
		1 4	2 7	3 10	4 13	5 16
6 19	7 22	8 25	9 28	10 31	11 34	12 37
13 40	14 43	15 46				

February Calendar Record Sheet		
Input Number	Output Number	Observations & Predictions
1	4	It added 3 today. Maybe it'll do that every time.
2	7	Now it added 5, not 3.
3	10	It added 7 this time.
4	13	Every new number on the Out side is 3 more than the one before.
5	16	Tomorrow it will be 19, and the day after, it will be 22. It's always 3 more.
6	19	It goes up by 1 on the In number and by 3 on the Out number.
7	22	I added 15 today. Tomorrow it will add 17. So the Out number will be 25, because 8·17·25
8	25	We were right. It added 17, because 8·17·25
9	28	It's an even number.
10	31	This is the same thing. It's 11·11·11·11·1 more to get to 34.
11	34	Odd number.
12	37	
13	40	Even number.
14	43	If you made a picture, it would be 3 legs of 14 one more. That's 43.
15	46	3·15·45. Add one more and it's 46.

February

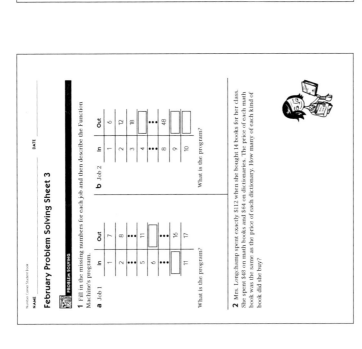

Quick Facts Worksheet

NAME Sage DATE 2/2

What's your multiplier?	How many minutes?	Number correct
6	4	

1 Multiply each number in the grid by your multiplier. Write each product in the box.

30 ^{5}	42 ^{7}	18 ^{3}	36 ^{6}	6 ^{1}	0 ^{0}	12 ^{2}	60 ^{10}
24 ^{4}	36 ^{6}	66 ^{11}	54 ^{9}	72 ^{12}	48 ^{8}	24 ^{4}	30 ^{5}
36 ^{6}	60 ^{10}	12 ^{2}	42 ^{7}	48 ^{8}	6 ^{1}	54 ^{9}	18 ^{3}
54 ^{9}	42 ^{7}	72 ^{12}	12 ^{2}	66 ^{11}	0 ^{0}	48 ^{8}	60 ^{10}
66 ^{11}	72 ^{12}	18 ^{3}	^{4}	^{7}	6 ^{1}	^{5}	^{9}

2 Choose 10 *different* products from above (except 0) and record them in the 10 boxes below. Then divide each by your multiplier.

$6\overline{)30}\ ^5$ $6\overline{)24}\ ^4$ $6\overline{)36}\ ^6$ $6\overline{)66}\ ^{11}$ $6\overline{)12}\ ^2$

$6\overline{)48}\ ^8$ $6\overline{)54}\ ^9$ $6\overline{)42}\ ^7$ $6\overline{)18}\ ^3$ $6\overline{)72}\ ^{12}$

Computational Fluency

Number Corner Student Book

NAME DATE

February Problem Solving Sheet 3

PROBLEM SOLVING

1 Fill in the missing numbers for each job and then describe the Function Machine's program.

a Job 1

In	Out
1	7
2	8
•••	•••
6	11
•••	•••
11	16
	17

What is the program?

b Job 2

In	Out
1	6
2	12
3	18
•••	•••
8	48
•••	•••
9	
10	

What is the program?

2 Mrs. Longchamp spent exactly $112 when she bought 14 books for her class. She spent $48 on math books and $64 on dictionaries. The price of each math book was the same as the price of each dictionary. How many of each kind of book did she buy?

Problem Solving

What's Going to Happen in February?

The workouts this month feature algebraic thinking, multi-step problem solving, and many opportunities to practice basic multiplication facts. The Calendar Grid serves as an introduction to functions: rules of correspondence and relationships between two sets of numbers. Some of the problems featured in the Problem Solving Workouts return to this idea, while others require multiple steps and operations to solve. The Number Line Workout provides opportunities for students to work with harder multiplication facts and to observe some of the patterns and relationships among them, while the Calendar Collector features a probability experiment in which students must apply their knowledge of basic multiplication facts. During the Computational Fluency Workout, students continue to work toward mastery of the multiplication facts, using the Quick Facts routine introduced last month.

Calendar Grid

Functions pervade mathematics, all the way from beginning experiences in the early grades through the work of research mathematicians. Already this year, your students have discovered and applied relationships between quarts and cups, meters and decimeters, and feet and inches. This month's Calendar Grid Workouts introduce the concept of functions, using the device of an imaginary function machine that transforms numbers in an unlimited number of ways, depending on how it is programmed. One number goes in, another comes out, and if you study a particular set of input and output numbers, you can identify a rule or "program" for determining the output value for any input value (or given the output value, the input value may not be unique). This rule or program is the function.

Each calendar marker features two numbers: the input number, which is the date, and the output number. Students will examine the markers, T-charts of the values on the markers, and arrangements of tile that represent each output number to determine the relationship between each input number and its corresponding output number. Ultimately, students will find that each output number is produced by multiplying the input number by 3 and adding 1.

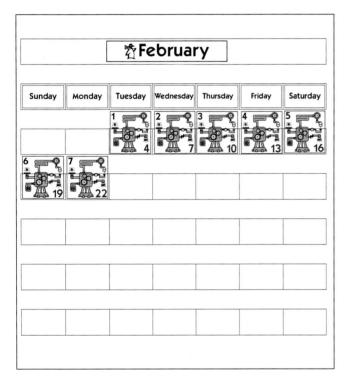

February Calendar Record Sheet

Input Number	Output Number	Observations & Predictions
1	4	Maybe it'll add 3 each time.
2	7	Now it added 5, not 3.
3	10	It added 7 this time.
4	13	Every new number on the Out side is 3 more than the one before.
5	16	Tomorrow it will be 10, and the day after, it will be 22. It's always 3 more.
6	19	It goes up by 1 on the In number and by 3 on the Out number.
7	22	The Out number is way more than double the In number. It's more like 3 times the In number.

February Overhead NC 6.7

Inside the Function Machine

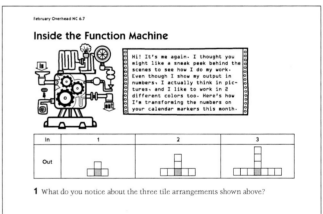

Hi! It's me again. I thought you might like a sneak peek behind the scenes to see how I do my work. Even though I show my output in numbers, I actually think in pictures, and I like to work in 2 different colors too. Here's how I'm transforming the numbers on your calendar markers this month.

1 What do you notice about the three tile arrangements shown above?

···

Calendar Collector

In this month's Calendar Collector, students collect data from repeated trials of a probability experiment in which they roll two dice marked 4–9 and then compute the product of the two numbers rolled. The question is whether odd and even products are equally likely, or whether one is more likely than the other. Students speculate about this question, use their data to make conjectures, and analyze the conditions of the experiment to draw conclusions about the probability of getting an odd or an even product with each roll.

Computational Fluency

Students continue with the Quick Facts routine introduced in January. Each week, students work with one multiplier of their choice until they can complete at least 38 facts for that multiplier correctly in 2 minutes or less. When they can, they move on to a new multiplier of their choice, with the ultimate goal of mastering the facts for all multipliers from 2 to 12.

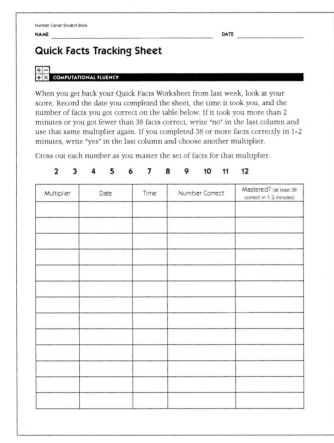

Problem Solving

This month, the Problem Solving Workouts feature multi-step computation and word problems, most of which revolve around multiplication and division. Students will likely find some of the problems this month more challenging than those offered in previous months. As they devise strategies for solving these problems, students will have opportunities to think outside the box and use their tools and skills in new ways to devise their own solution methods.

In many districts, students are expected to understand and use specific strategies for solving problems, the most common of which are listed below.

• acting out the situation or using objects

• making a sketch or a picture

- using or looking for a pattern
- making an organized list
- using or making a table or a chart
- using logical reasoning—working from things they know to things they don't know
- guess and check

Students will generate many of these strategies on their own if given time and the appropriate materials. However, some guidance is offered this month, and more guidance is provided in future months, for introducing and classifying these strategies for students as needed.

Number Line

Students examine multiples of 8 and 9. They consider whether if they went back and marked all the multiples of 8 and 9 on the Number Line they would mark any number that hasn't yet been identified as a multiple of 2–7. This activity provides an opportunity to work with multiplication facts for 8 and 9 and investigate intriguing number patterns among multiples of different numbers.

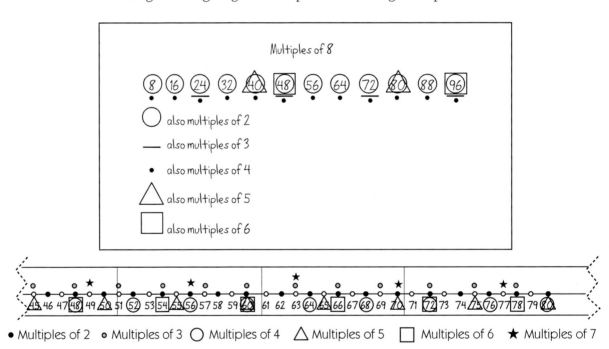

Planning for February

You can use the planning guide below as shown or adapt it to fit the needs of your students and schedule. You can also use the planner template (Blackline NC 1.1) to plan this month of workouts day by day.

FEBRUARY PLANNING GUIDE						
Key ★ = Discuss ☆ = Update SB = Number Corner Student Book	MON	TUES	WED	THURS	FRI	SB
Calendar Grid, pp. 227–232 The Function Machine • describing, extending, and making generalizations about number patterns • representing and analyzing patterns and functions • describing the rule governing the relationship between two values in a table	★	☆	☆	☆	★	p. 68
Calendar Collector, pp. 233–237 Roll & Multiply • using multiplication facts through 9 × 9 with fluency • describing the probability of various outcomes or events • constructing, reading, and interpreting bar graphs	☆	★	☆	☆	☆	pp. 63, 65, and 69
Computational Fluency, pp. 238–240 Quick Facts • fluently using multiplication facts through 12 × 12 • developing efficient strategies for solving basic division facts			★			p. 50
Problem Solving, pp. 241–245 Solving More Complex Problems • using different models of division to solve problems • multiplying and dividing 2- and 3-digit numbers by 1-digit numbers • describing the rule governing the relationship between two values in a table • solving multi-step story problems using a variety of efficient paper/pencil and mental strategies				★		pp. 61, 64, and 66
Number Line, pp. 246–250 Multiples of 8 & 9 • exploring factors of whole numbers through 100 • using multiplication facts through 10 × 10 with fluency • describing, extending, and making generalizations about numeric and geometric patterns	☆	☆	☆	☆	★	pp. 62 and 67

Materials You'll Need for February

MANIPULATIVES & MATERIALS

Manipulatives
- Calendar Grid pocket chart
- 2 dice marked 4–9
- 1 pair of dice numbered 1–6 for each pair of students
- calculators
- 10 colored tile in one color and 20 in another color for each pair of students (Cut construction paper or poster board in 2 different colors into 1" squares to make your own tile if needed.)
- counters such as tile or base ten units

Number Corner Calendar Markers
- Day, Month, and Year markers
- Function Machine calendar markers

Number Corner Components
- Number Line

General Materials
- black felt-tip marker
- yellow highlighter marker
- overhead pens or Vis-à-Vis pens in several colors
- piece of paper to mask parts of the overhead
- a few blank overhead transparencies
- pointer (such as a yard or meter stick)
- crayons

ADVANCE PREPARATION

Calendar Grid

Run 1 copy each of Blacklines NC 6.1 and 6.2. Trim and then glue or tape them together to form one long chart. Post on your calendar display board before you conduct your first Calendar Grid Workout this month. Also, if you don't have colored tile, cut 2 different colors of construction paper or poster board into 1" squares before your third workout. Each pair of students will need 10 squares in one color and 20 in another color.

Calendar Collector

Run 1 copy each of Blacklines NC 6.3 and 6.4. Trim and then glue or tape them together to form one long chart. Post on your calendar display board before conducting your first Calendar Collector Workout this month. You can also run a class set if you want each student to keep a record.

BLACKLINES & OVERHEADS

Number Corner Overheads

NC 5.1	Quick Facts Worksheet
NC 5.2	Quick Facts Tracking Sheet
NC 6.1	Introducing the Function Machine
NC 6.2	February Problem Solving Sheet 1
NC 6.3	Problem Solving Solution Page
NC 6.4	Multiples of 8
NC 6.5	Roll & Multiply Data Chart
NC 6.6	February Problem Solving Sheet 2
NC 6.7	Inside the Function Machine
NC 6.8	February Problem Solving Sheet 3
NC 6.9	Extending the Function Machine Pattern

Number Corner Blacklines

NC 1.1	Monthly Planner Template (1 copy, optional)
NC 5.6	Quick Facts Worksheet (4 class sets)
NC 6.1 & 6.2	February Calendar Grid Record Sheet, pages 1 and 2 (1 copy each)
NC 6.3 & 6.4	Roll & Multiply Record Sheet, pages 1 and 2 (1 copy each)
NC 6.5	Problem Solving Solution Page (3 class sets, optional)
NC 6.6	February Problem Strips (class set, optional)
NC 6.7–6.9	Days of School Beyond 100 Record Sheet, pages 1–3 (1 copy each, optional)

Number Corner Student Book

page 50	Quick Facts Tracking Sheet
page 61	February Problem Solving Sheet 1
page 62	Multiples of 8
page 63	Roll & Multiply Data Chart
page 64	February Problem Solving Sheet 2
page 65	Thinking about Roll & Multiply
page 66	February Problem Solving Sheet 3
page 67	Multiples of 9
page 68	Extending the Function Machine Pattern
page 69	One More Look at Roll & Multiply

February Calendar Grid

CALENDAR GRID

The Function Machine

Overview

After an introduction to the concept of functions, a new marker is added to the Calendar Grid each day and an entry made on a record sheet that accompanies the grid. Students discuss the grid and the record sheet as a whole group twice this month. They work together during the latter part of the month to look at the calendar pattern in a visual form that will lend depth and insight to their observations and generalizations.

Frequency

Update the Calendar Grid each day and share observations and predictions at least once a week.

Skills & Concepts

★ describing, extending, and making generalizations about number patterns

★ representing and analyzing patterns and functions

★ describing the rule governing the relationship between two values in a table

You'll need

★ Introducing the Function Machine (Overhead NC 6.1)

★ Inside the Function Machine (Overhead NC 6.7)

★ Extending the Function Machine Pattern (Overhead NC 6.9)

★ February Calendar Grid Record Sheet, pages 1 and 2 (Blacklines NC 6.1 and 6.2, see Advance Preparation)

★ Extending the Function Machine Pattern (Number Corner Student Book, page 68)

★ Calendar Grid pocket chart

★ Day, Month, and Year markers

★ Function Machine calendar markers

★ colored tile or 2 different colors of construction paper or poster board cut into 1″ squares (Each pair will need about 10 squares in one color and 20 in another color.)

STUDENT BOOK

....

Advance Preparation Run 1 copy each of Blacklines NC 6.1 and 6.2. Trim and then glue or tape them together to form one long chart. Post on your calendar display board before you conduct your first Calendar Grid Workout this month. Also, if you don't have colored tile, cut 2 different colors of construction paper or poster board into 1″ squares before your third workout. Each pair of students will need 10 squares in one color and 20 in another color.

....

Calendar Grid The Function Machine (cont.)

....

Background for Teachers *This month's Calendar Grid introduces the algebraic concept of a function. Although the mathematical definition of a function—a* relationship between two variables in which the value of one variable, often called the output, depends on the value of the other, often called the input— *sounds a bit technical, your students have had many informal experiences with functions already, both in daily life and in school. For instance, most fourth graders will be able to tell quickly that 20 bicycles have 40 wheels altogether, because they know that 1 bicycle has 2 wheels, 2 bicycles have 4 wheels, 3 bicycles have 6 wheels, and so on. To find the number of wheels on any number of bicycles, you just multiply the number of bicycles by 2, or, as children are more likely to say, you just double the number of bicycles to get the number of wheels. This pattern holds for any number of bicycles, and the relationship between these two quantities—the number of bicycles and the number of wheels—is a* function.

....

....

Week 1 Introducing the Function Machine & the New Markers

Open your first Calendar Grid Workout this month by displaying the Introducing the Function Machine overhead. Read the text at the top out loud and complete the two T-charts with the class, and then ask them to describe the "program" for each job (e.g., the rule that's at work) using words and/or numbers. If it seems appropriate at this time, you might model for students how their equations or expressions could be represented algebraically ($n + 2$ for Job 1 and $n \times 2$ or $2n$ for Job 2).

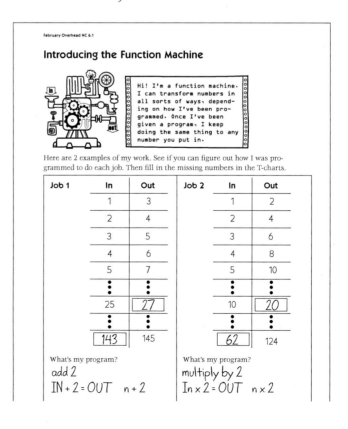

Calendar Grid The Function Machine (cont.)

Now ask a volunteer to post the calendar markers for each day that has passed so far this month, including today. Then, with students' input, write the input and output numbers on the Calendar Grid Record Sheet so they can be seen in T-chart form. Invite students to share observations about the marker(s) and record those observations in the last column on the record sheet.

Week 2 Discussing the Markers & Adding Information to the Record Sheet

Open the second workout by asking students to discuss and predict, first in pairs, and then as a whole group, what the two numbers on today's marker will be. Ask them to share not only their predictions, but also their reasoning about the numbers they suggest. Encourage them also to make generalizations about the relationship between the input and the output numbers.

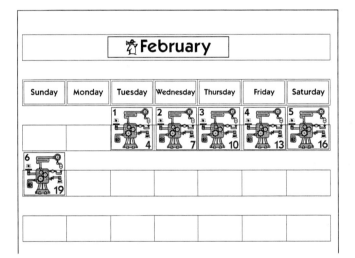

February Calendar Record Sheet		
Input Number	Output Number	Observations & Predictions
1	4	It added 3 today. Maybe it'll do that every time.
2	7	Now it added 5, not 3.
3	10	It added 7 this time.
4	13	Every new number on the Out side is 3 more than the one before.
5	16	Tomorrow it will be 19, and the day after, it will be 22. It's always 3 more.
6	19	It goes up by 1 on the In number and by 3 on the Out number.

Students *The marker for today will have a 7 for the "in" number because today is February 7th. The "in" number always matches the date. The "out" number will be red. They always are. And we think it will be 22 because it's always 3 more, and 19 plus 3 is 22.*
We said the same thing. The pattern on the "in" numbers is 1, 2, 3, 4, 5, 6, 7. They just go up by 1. The pattern on the "out" numbers is 4, 7, 10, 13, 16, 19. They go up by 3 every time, so we think today's "out" number will be 22.

Teacher *Why do you think the output numbers keep increasing by 3?*

Students *Because that's the pattern.*
It's just how the machine is working.
You can just see. It's 4, then 7, then 10, then 13. 4 plus 3 is 7; 7 plus 3 is 10. With today's number, it's going to be 19 plus 3, and that will be 22.

Calendar Grid The Function Machine (cont.)

Teacher *So can we say that the machine is adding 3 to each input number to get the output number?*

Students *Yes!*
No! The "out" numbers keep getting 3 bigger each time, but it's not adding 3 to each "in" number.
But 1 plus 3 is 4 on the first marker.
Look at the second one, though. If it was just adding 3 to every "in" number, the "out" number for 2 would be 5, and the "out" number for 3 would be 6. But they're not.

Teacher *So what is it doing to the "in" number to get the "out" number? Let's say the "in" number was 30. What would be the "out" number, and how do you know?*

Students *33.*
No way. We're on the 6th and the out numbers are already at 19. So for the 30th, it'll be way more than 33.
Umm. I don't know. Let's keep adding 3 until we get to the 30th.
There has to be a faster way.
If we knew what the function machine was doing to the "in" numbers, we could figure it out right away.

After some discussion, post the marker for the day and bring the record sheet up to date. Your class may not articulate the function machine's program quite yet, and that is alright. They will have the rest of the month to think about it.

Week 3 Using Tile to Explore the Pattern

As you begin your third Calendar Grid Workout, distribute tile, or construction paper or poster board squares, to students (each pair will need about 10 in one color and 20 in another color) and display the Inside the Function Machine overhead. Read the text at the top out loud and then reveal the three arrangements of tile directly below the text.

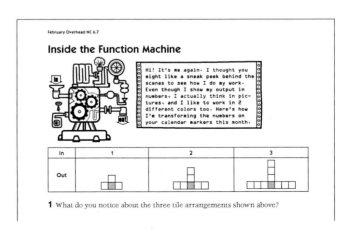

Calendar Grid The Function Machine (cont.)

Ask student pairs to build these three arrangements of tile at their desks using one color for the center piece and a second color for the arms. Then give them time to pair-share observations before having volunteers share their thinking with the class. Use the space provided on the transparency to record students' observations.

> **Students** *There are always three arms with one in the middle.*
> *There are 3 more squares every time: 4, 7, 10.*
> *Even number of tile, odd number of tile, even number of tile.*
> *It is a growing pattern.*
> *The 2nd has 2 going out on each arm and the 3rd has 3 going out on each arm.*
> *I see 1 going up and 3 across the bottom, 2 going up and 5 across, 3 up and 7 across.*
> *The tiles going up go 1, 2, 3.*

After students have had a chance to share their observations, ask them to work in pairs to build the fourth and fifth arrangements in the sequence. Students may propose extending the pattern in a few ways, but many will probably build the 2 arrangements shown below.

4th arrangement   5th arrangement

If you have time, acknowledge and discuss other ideas, but return quickly to the arrangements above. Be sure to have several pairs explain why they extended the pattern in this way, because their explanations, along with the observations they made about the first three arrangements, will pave the way to making generalizations about the pattern. On the overhead, model how to record the arrangements using quick sketches as shown below.

Finally, ask students to determine the total number of tile in the fifth arrangement. Record their thinking on the overhead using equations and a quick-sketch of the arrangement itself. Their equations hold the key to discovering the function on the calendar pattern.

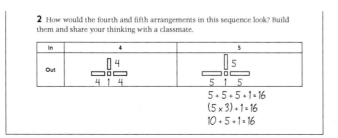

Calendar Grid The Function Machine (cont.)

If students don't bring it up, call their attention to the calendar markers at this point. Can they see any connection between the number of tile in each arrangement and the output numbers on the markers? This discussion may require a bit more time than you usually allot for Number Corner, but it will help students take a deeper look at the patterns that are emerging on the Calendar Grid.

⋯⋯⋯⋯⋯⋯⋯⋯⋯⋯⋯⋯⋯⋯⋯⋯⋯⋯⋯⋯⋯⋯⋯⋯⋯⋯⋯⋯⋯⋯⋯⋯⋯⋯⋯⋯⋯⋯

Note *If you have cut construction paper or poster board squares for this workout, be sure to save them for use next week.*

⋯⋯⋯⋯⋯⋯⋯⋯⋯⋯⋯⋯⋯⋯⋯⋯⋯⋯⋯⋯⋯⋯⋯⋯⋯⋯⋯⋯⋯⋯⋯⋯⋯⋯⋯⋯⋯⋯

⋯⋯⋯⋯⋯⋯⋯⋯⋯⋯⋯⋯⋯⋯⋯⋯⋯⋯⋯⋯⋯⋯⋯⋯⋯⋯⋯⋯⋯⋯⋯⋯⋯⋯⋯⋯⋯⋯

Week 4 Extending the Function Machine Pattern

During the fourth Calendar Grid Workout, ask students to pair up to work on page 68 in the Number Corner Student Book. Although they'll work in pairs, ask students to complete their own pages. Make colored tile, or construction paper or poster board squares, available for those who want to use them. Remind students to use quick sketches to show their predictions about the fourth, fifth, and tenth arrangements instead of drawing every single tile.

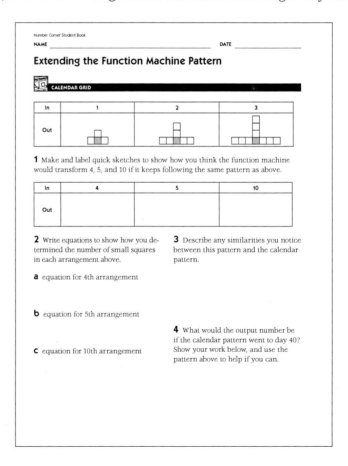

When students have completed the page, invite them to discuss their answers to questions 3 and 4.

February Calendar Collector

CALENDAR COLLECTOR

Roll & Multiply

STUDENT BOOK   TECHNOLOGY CONNECTION

Overview

This month, students collect data from repeated trials of a probability experiment in which they roll two dice marked 4–9 and multiply the two numbers. Before conducting the experiment, they predict how likely it is that a given product will be odd and how likely it is to be even. In the middle of the month, after conducting 5 trials every day, students revise their predictions and then continue making 5 trials a day through the end of the month.

Frequency

Update the data daily, and share observations and predictions about the data as a whole group once or twice a week.

Skills & Concepts

★ using multiplication facts through 9×9 with fluency

★ predicting the probability of various outcomes or events

★ representing all possible outcomes for a simple probability situation

★ conducting a probability experiment

★ constructing, reading, and interpreting bar graphs

You'll need

★ Roll & Multiply Data Chart (Overhead NC 6.5)

★ Roll & Multiply Record Sheet, pages 1 and 2 (Blacklines NC 6.3 and 6.4, 1 copy each, see Advance Preparation)

★ Roll & Multiply Data Chart (Number Corner Student Book, page 63)

★ Thinking about Roll & Multiply (Number Corner Student Book, page 65)

★ One More Look at Roll & Multiply (Number Corner Student Book, page 69)

★ 2 dice marked 4–9

★ calculators

★ black felt-tip marker

★ yellow highlighter marker

★ overhead pens

Advance Preparation Run 1 copy each of Blacklines NC 6.3 and 6.4. Trim and then glue or tape them together to form one long chart. Post on your calendar display board before conducting your first Calendar Collector Workout this month. You can also run a class set if you want each student to keep a record.

Week 1 Introducing Roll & Multiply

Introduce Roll & Multiply by holding up two dice marked 4–9. Ask students what the chance of getting an odd product would be if you rolled the two dice and multiplied the numbers that came up. What would be the chance of getting an even product? Is there a better chance of getting one than the other, or is it equally likely that you'll get an odd or an even product? What if you repeated the experiment 100 times? Would you get odd products more often

Calendar Collector Roll & Multiply (cont.)

than even, even more often than odd, or about the same number of odd and even products? Give students time to consider these questions and discuss their reasoning in pairs and as a whole group.

Explain that they will conduct 5 trials of this experiment for each day in February, including weekends and holidays. Then ask them to discuss the following questions:

- How many rolls will that be in all? (5 rolls per day × 28 days = 140 rolls or 5 rolls per day × 29 days = 145 rolls)
- Does the class really need to collect that much data? How much do they think is enough to determine the chances of rolling an odd or an even product?
- How many rolls will they need to make today? (The number of rolls will depend on how many days have passed already this month.)

Finally, have students roll and multiply as you record the products on the Calendar Collector Record Sheet. You might do this by calling students up one by one or having them pass the 2 dice from student to student. After recording all of the products, ask students to classify each one as odd or even, and highlight the odd products with a colored marker. Finally, ask them to count how many odd and even products they got in each group of 5 trials, and record those totals on the record sheet. Some students may have difficulty identifying whether these larger numbers are odd or even. If so, take some time for students to discuss how they can tell. Some may think about dividing each by 2, while others may see that they can refer to the number line to see if each number is marked as a multiple of 2. At some point, some students may also see that if one of the multipliers is even, the product will also be even.

	Roll & Multiply Record Sheet						
Day	**Products**					**Number of Odd Products**	**Number of Even Products**
1	42	20	20	30	63	1	4
2	40	64	72	45	36	1	4
3							
4							
5							
6							
7							

To conclude the first workout, ask students to share observations and predictions about the likely outcomes of this experiment over the course of the month. Based on the data they collected today, many fourth-graders will suggest that they will get more even than odd products but may not be able to explain why. Others may be convinced that they are just as likely to roll an even or odd product, because there are 3 odd and 3 even numbers on each die.

Calendar Collector Roll & Multiply (cont.)

Week 2 Showing the Data on a Chart & Graph

Before conducting the second Calendar Collector Workout, have a student helper make sure the record sheet is up to date. Then have another student or pair of students find the total number of times odd and even products have been rolled and enter those totals on the overhead Roll & Multiply Data Chart. Emphasize that this task needs to be done carefully and accurately. You may want to check students' work quickly before proceeding with the workout.

Day	Products					Number of Odd Products	Number of Even Products
1	42	20	20	30	63	1	4
2	40	64	72	45	36	1	4
3	20	48	28	54	54	0	5
4	32	16	81	54	42	1	4
5	54	48	25	81	35	3	2
6	48	35	64	20	72	1	4
7	48	72	49	63	35	3	2
8	72	45	63	54	32	2	3
9							
10							
11							
12							
13							
14							

Roll & Multiply Record Sheet

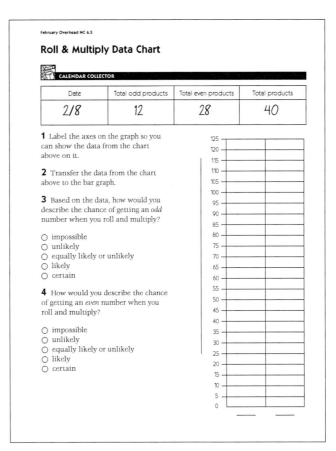

Display the Roll & Multiply Data Chart with the totals filled in at the top. Give students a few minutes to share observations and conjectures about the data, and then ask them to think about how they can transfer the data to the bar graph on the overhead. Remind them that they need to label both axes of the graph and ask them to decide together what those labels should say. When they have decided, label the axes on the overhead.

Then read questions 2 and 3 together and have students share their current understandings of the terms *impossible, unlikely, equally likely or unlikely, likely,* and *certain.* Students' understandings of these terms are often intuitive at this time of year, and that is fine. Next, have students complete page 63 in their Student Books, which is identical to the overhead. They will need to fill in the

Calendar Collector Roll & Multiply (cont.)

totals, label the axes, and then fill in the bar graph with the totals and answer questions 2 and 3.

As they finish working on their sheets, have students meet in pairs to compare their graphs and the ways they described the probability of getting odds and evens. They'll discuss these ideas further in the workout next week.

Week 3 Thinking about the Data So Far

Before conducting the third Calendar Collector Workout, have a student helper make sure the record sheet is up to date. Then have another student or pair of students find the total number of odd and even products that have been rolled so far. Ask them to enter those totals on the overhead Roll & Multiply Data Chart. By now, the data should show that even products come up far more frequently than odd products.

Display the overhead with the totals filled in and give students a couple of minutes to share observations and conjectures about the data. Then ask them to complete page 65 in their Student Books.

The multiplication table on the page will help students see that the chances of rolling an odd product are 9 out of 36 (or 1 out of 4) and the chances of rolling an even product are 27 out of 36 (or 3 out of 4). While fourth graders may not express these probabilities in numerical form, the sheet will help them begin to see why they have gotten more even than odd products.

Calendar Collector Roll & Multiply (cont.)

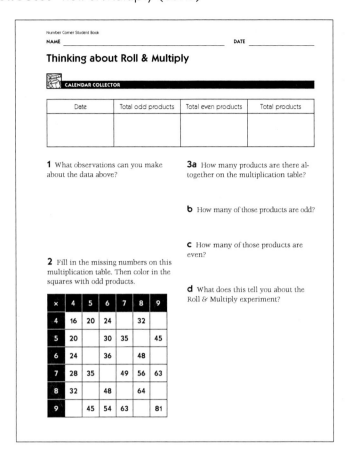

As they finish working on their sheets, have students meet in pairs to compare and discuss their work, especially their responses to the final question. When everyone is finished, ask them to discuss the last question as a class.

Week 4 Drawing Conclusions about the Data & the Experiment

Before you conduct the last Calendar Collector Workout, record on the Roll & Multiply Data Chart overhead the total number of times odd and even products have come up so far this month. To open the last workout, display the overhead with the totals filled in and invite students to share observations. Then ask them to think about how the total number of odd products relates to the total number of even products. (It is likely that students will notice that there are about 3 times as many even products as odd products and that about a fourth of all the products are odd.) After students have had a chance to discuss the results as a whole group, have them complete page 69 in their Student Books.

If there are still a few days remaining in the month, ask students to think about whether the additional data is likely to alter their conclusions. Have student helpers continue to collect and record data through the remainder of the month, and if there is time and high student interest, take a few minutes at the very end of the month to re-examine the totals one last time.

February Computational Fluency

COMPUTATIONAL FLUENCY

Quick Facts

Overview

Students continue the Quick Facts routine introduced in January. As they did last month, students choose their own multipliers, which they'll work with until they can complete 40 facts correctly in 2 minutes or less. Each time they reach that level of fluency, they'll choose another multiplier, working toward the goal of mastering their multiplication facts through 12 × 12. If your state standards require fluency to 10 × 10, you can adjust the goals of this workout for your class.

Frequency

One day per week

Skills & Concepts

★ fluently using multiplication facts through 12 × 12

★ developing efficient strategies for solving basic division facts

★ relating multiplication and division

You'll need

★ Quick Facts Worksheet (Overhead NC 5.1)

★ Quick Facts Tracking Sheet (Overhead NC 5.2)

★ Quick Facts Worksheet (Blackline NC 5.6, 4 class sets)

★ Quick Facts Tracking Sheet (Number Corner Student Book, page 50)

★ 1 pair of dice numbered 1–6 for each pair of students

At the start of each workout, return students' corrected Quick Facts Worksheets from the previous week and have them enter the information on their Quick Facts Tracking Sheet (page 50 in their Student Books). If they completed at least 38 of the 40 facts correctly in 2 minutes or less, they can move along to another multiplier. If not, they'll need to use the same multiplier this week.

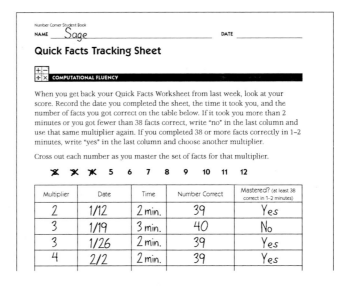

Computational Fluency Quick Facts (cont.)

After they have recorded the results of the previous week's Quick Facts exercise, give students about 5 minutes to practice their chosen set of facts before starting the worksheet. There are many quick and simple ways to do this. Here are just a few ideas:

- Have students write their own set of flashcards on the spot and then "test" each other.
- Give each pair of students 2 dice numbered 1–6. Have them announce their multipliers to each other and then take turns rolling the 2 dice, adding the 2 numbers, and multiplying the sum by their multiplier.
- Have students list the facts for their multiplier several times on a piece of paper.
- If your classroom is equipped with computers, students can play a quick multiplication practice game electronically.

After they have had a few minutes to practice, reconvene the class and distribute copies of the Quick Facts Worksheet. Have students record their names, the date, and their multiplier before they begin. Then write a "0–1" on the board, give the signal to start, and let students go to work as quickly and accurately as they can while you watch the clock. After a minute has passed, write "1–2" on the board. After 2 minutes have passed, record "2–3." After 3 minutes have passed, write "3–4," and after 4 minutes have passed, call time.

January Blackline NC 5.6 Run 4 class sets.

NAME _Sage_ DATE _2/2_

Quick Facts Worksheet

What's your multiplier?	How many minutes?	Number correct
6	4	

1 Multiply each number in the grid by your multiplier. Write each product in the box.

5	7	3	6	1	0	2	10
30	42	18	36	6	0	12	60

4	6	11	9	12	8	4	5
24	36	66	54	72	48	24	30

6	10	2	7	8	1	9	3
36	60	12	42	48	6	54	18

9	7	12	2	11	0	8	10
54	42	72	12	66	0	48	60

11	12	3	4	7	6	5	9
66	72	18					

2 Choose 10 *different* products from above (except 0) and record them in the 10 boxes below. Then divide each by your multiplier.

Computational Fluency Quick Facts (cont.)

As soon as they have completed the 40 facts, students should turn their paper over, look up at the board, and record the last number you wrote. If they have not completed the 40 problems when time is called, ask them to stop, even if they're not finished, and write a 4 in the appropriate space at the top of the sheet.

Finally, have them complete the bottom section of the Quick Facts sheet by choosing 10 different products from the grid above, entering each in one of the dividend boxes, and then dividing each by the multiplier.

As students finish, collect their papers and remind the class that you'll return the sheets the following week, corrected and ready to be entered on their Quick Facts Tracking Sheet.

CHALLENGE

If you find that some students know all their facts, give them alternate tasks during this workout for the next couple of months. They might serve as tutors for students who are having a difficult time, or they might work independently on some of the problems from the Problem Solving Workout. Another option is to have them play Roll 5, a game that uses all 4 operations and is nearly unlimited in terms of challenge level. The instructions and several copies of the record sheet for this game can be found in the Number Corner Student Book, pages 51–54.

SUPPORT

While we want all fourth graders to be fluent with their multiplication facts by the end of the school year, some students will not reach this goal without considerable support. If some students are still working with 2's or 3's, and struggling to do so, you may want to have them play some of the support games listed after the January Number Corner Checkup with a paraprofessional, resource room teacher, or parent. There are also many engaging software programs designed to help students practice basic facts, and you can certainly give students copies of the Quick Facts sheets to use for home practice during the week as well.

February Problem Solving

PROBLEM SOLVING

Solving More Complex Problems

Overview

This month, the Problem Solving Workouts feature multi-step computation and word problems, most of which revolve around multiplication and division. Because the problems are more complex, there are only two to a page instead of four, and because the month is short, there are only three workouts planned instead of four.

Frequency

One day per week

Skills & Concepts

★ using different models of division to solve problems

★ multiplying and dividing 2- and 3-digit numbers by 1-digit numbers

★ describing the rule governing the relationship between two values in a table

★ selecting methods and tools appropriate to a particular context for operations with whole numbers

★ solving multi-step story problems using a variety of efficient paper/pencil and mental strategies

You'll need

★ February Problem Solving Sheets 1–3 (Overheads NC 6.2, 6.6, and 6.8)

★ Problem Solving Solution Page (Overhead NC 6.3)

★ Problem Solving Solution Page (Blackline NC 6.5, 3 class sets, optional)

★ February Problem Strips (Blackline NC 6.6, class set, optional)

★ February Problem Solving Sheets 1–3 (Number Corner Student Book, pages 61, 64, and 66)

★ counters such as tile or base ten units

★ calculators

★ piece of paper to mask parts of the overhead

★ overhead pens

★ a few blank overhead transparencies

Background for Teachers *You and your students will likely notice that the problems this month are more challenging than many of those offered in previous months. A true problem—in the realm of math, science, social interaction, or any other area of human endeavor—involves a situation we don't already know how to handle and that compels us to draw upon previous knowledge to formulate a strategy that will yield a solution. By its nature, problem solving is both exhilarating and frustrating, because it requires us to do something we don't already know how to do. As they devise strategies for solving the problems this month, students will think outside the box and use their tools and skills in new ways. You'll probably find that this takes time, patience, and perseverance.*

Problem Solving Solving More Complex Problems (cont.)

Conducting the Workouts Each Week

Each week, ask students to turn to the next Problem Solving page in their Number Corner Student Books. Invite each student to begin working on the one problem on the sheet that interests him most and to complete both problems only if there is time. Make all tools, including manipulatives and calculators, available and encourage students to use whichever ones they find helpful. (The only exception is that students should not use a calculator to solve the first problem on the second sheet, because it involves a chain of computations that build on one another.) Some students may also prefer to work in pairs, which is fine.

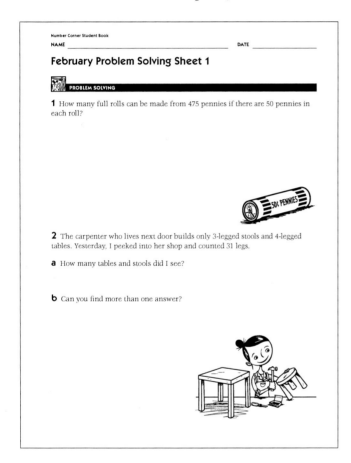

Number Corner Student Book
NAME _____ DATE _____

February Problem Solving Sheet 1

PROBLEM SOLVING

1 How many full rolls can be made from 475 pennies if there are 50 pennies in each roll?

2 The carpenter who lives next door builds only 3-legged stools and 4-legged tables. Yesterday, I peeked into her shop and counted 31 legs.

a How many tables and stools did I see?

b Can you find more than one answer?

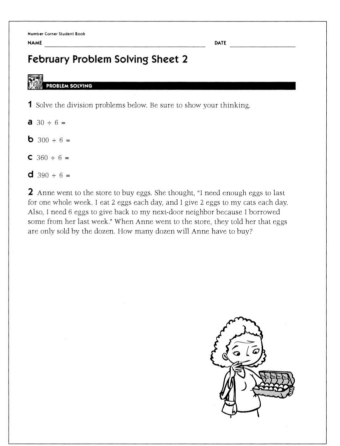

Number Corner Student Book
NAME _____ DATE _____

February Problem Solving Sheet 2

PROBLEM SOLVING

1 Solve the division problems below. Be sure to show your thinking.

a $30 \div 6 =$

b $300 \div 6 =$

c $360 \div 6 =$

d $390 \div 6 =$

2 Anne went to the store to buy eggs. She thought, "I need enough eggs to last for one whole week. I eat 2 eggs each day, and I give 2 eggs to my cats each day. Also, I need 6 eggs to give back to my next-door neighbor because I borrowed some from her last week." When Anne went to the store, they told her that eggs are only sold by the dozen. How many dozen will Anne have to buy?

When they have had time to complete one problem, ask them to discuss one or both problems as a class. As you have in past months, encourage them to take the lead in the class discussion. Because most of these problems will pose a significant challenge to many, if not most, students, the discussions are likely to be more interesting and animated than ever. You may find that students need to return to a problem the following week. You might also want to invite students to take these problems home or work on them during spare moments during the day.

Problem Solving Solving More Complex Problems (cont.)

Introducing the Problem Solving Solution Page (Optional)

Beginning this month, a sheet is provided to help students structure their responses to problems that will become increasingly challenging. If you feel that students would benefit from the additional structure this sheet offers, introduce it the first week, perhaps when students are discussing their solutions to the first problem on the first February Problem Solving Sheet. You can post the Problem Solving Solution Page overhead, which features the first problem on the first page, and go through the steps together with your class.

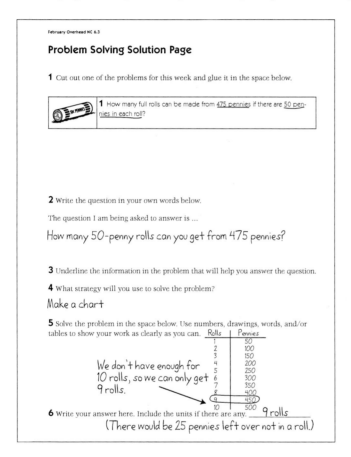

If you want to use this page, give students the sheet of Problem Strips each week, along with scissors and glue, so that they can use the Problem Solving Solution Page to structure their responses to the problems they want to solve. Some problems, like the first problems on the second and third sheets this month, do not lend themselves to this format, so no strip is provided for them.

Problem Solving Solving More Complex Problems (cont.)

February Blackline NC 6.5 Run class sets as needed from February through June. Optional.

NAME _____ DATE _____

Problem Solving Solution Page

1 Cut out one of the problems for this week and glue it in the space below.

2 Write the question in your own words below.

The question I am being asked to answer is …

3 Underline the information in the problem that will help you answer the question.

4 What strategy will you use to solve the problem?

5 Solve the problem in the space below. Use numbers, drawings, words, and/or tables to show your work as clearly as you can.

6 Write your answer here. Include the units if there are any. _____

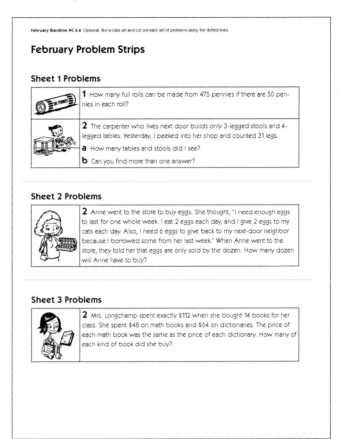

February Blackline NC 6.6 Optional. Run a class set and cut out each set of problems along the dotted lines.

February Problem Strips

Sheet 1 Problems

1 How many full rolls can be made from 475 pennies if there are 50 pennies in each roll?

2 The carpenter who lives next door builds only 3-legged stools and 4-legged tables. Yesterday, I peeked into her shop and counted 31 legs.

a How many tables and stools did I see?

b Can you find more than one answer?

Sheet 2 Problems

2 Anne went to the store to buy eggs. She thought, "I need enough eggs to last for one whole week. I eat 2 eggs each day, and I give 2 eggs to my cats each day. Also, I need 6 eggs to give back to my next-door neighbor because I borrowed some from her last week." When Anne went to the store, they told her that eggs are only sold by the dozen. How many dozen will Anne have to buy?

Sheet 3 Problems

2 Mrs. Longchamp spent exactly $112 when she bought 14 books for her class. She spent $48 on math books and $64 on dictionaries. The price of each math book was the same as the price of each dictionary. How many of each kind of book did she buy?

Getting Stuck

In attempting to solve these problems, students will probably get stuck sometimes, as we all do when solving genuine problems. Encourage them to ask each other for help when they get stuck, and model for students how they can share part of their thinking, describe the strategies they used, or give clues without revealing the answer to the person who needs help.

Students' initial attempts, conversations with partners, and whole-class discussions may produce more questions and puzzlements than answers, and the class may walk away from a problem one week and return to it the next. Celebrate students' efforts, even if they are only able to get a toe in the door when it comes to solving a given problem.

....

*A **Note about Teaching Specific Problem-Solving Strategies** When solving problems of all kinds, fourth graders will generate a variety of strategies and will generally try to be as efficient as they can. At times, however, you may want to name and classify the strategies students generate. You might also choose to introduce strategies that students don't generate on their own, especially if they seem to be stuck on one or two strategies in particular (guess and check is a great favorite with fourth graders) or if your school or district expects students to be able to name the strategies they are using and/or use a variety of strategies fluently.*

Problem Solving Solving More Complex Problems (cont.)

Here is a list of the problem-solving strategies most commonly used by and taught to fourth graders:

- *acting out the situation or using objects to model the situation*
- *making a sketch or a picture*
- *using or looking for a pattern*
- *making an organized list*
- *using or making a table or chart*
- *using logical reasoning—working from things they know to things they don't know*
- *guess and check*

More guidance is offered about addressing these strategies in next month's Problem Solving Workout. For now, you may want to give students space and time to develop their own strategies, many of which will resemble those listed above. Next month you might begin naming the strategies explicitly and introducing those strategies students have not begun to develop on their own.

February Number Line

NUMBER LINE

TECHNOLOGY CONNECTION

STUDENT BOOK

Multiples of 8 & 9

Overview

Students examine multiples of 8 and 9. They consider whether if they went back and marked all the multiples of 8 and 9 on the Number Line they would mark any number that hasn't yet been identified as a multiple of 2–7. (Students will not actually mark these multiples on the Number Line, which will be too crowded at this point.) This activity provides an opportunity to work with multiplication facts for 8 and 9 and investigate intriguing number patterns.

Frequency

Update the Number Line each day and do a whole-group workout once a week.

Skills & Concepts

★ exploring factors of whole numbers through 100

★ using multiplication facts through 10 × 10 with fluency

★ describing, extending, and making generalizations about numeric patterns

You'll need

★ Multiples of 8 (Overhead NC 6.4)

★ Days of School Beyond 100 Record Sheet, pages 1–3 (Blacklines NC 6.7–6.9, 1 copy each, optional, see page 249 for more information)

★ Multiples of 8 (Number Corner Student Book, page 62)

★ Multiples of 9 (Number Corner Student Book, page 67)

★ number line

★ calculators

★ pointer (such as a yard or meter stick)

★ erasable marking pens (overhead or Vis-à-Vis pens in several colors)

★ crayons

Week 1 Updating the Number Line & Completing a Student Book Page

In the first workout, take a few minutes to update and discuss the Number Line. Ask students whether the next number they will enter will be a multiple of 2, 3, 4, 5, 6, and/or 7. How do they know? If they're not sure, how can they find out?

Then pose the following question: If we went back and marked all the multiples of 8, would we mark any number that hasn't yet been marked? After just a minute or two of discussion and debate, display the Multiples of 8 overhead and ask students to turn to page 62 in their Number Corner Student Books. Read the directions out loud and then ask students to work independently

Number Line Multiples of 8 & 9 (cont.)

on the page. Let them know you'll discuss their answers and reasoning next week, so they'll need to save their completed sheets.

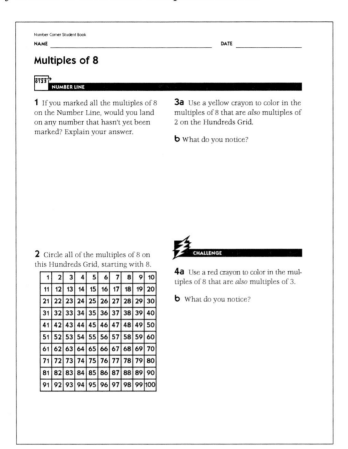

Number Corner Student Book

NAME _____ DATE _____

Multiples of 8

NUMBER LINE

1 If you marked all the multiples of 8 on the Number Line, would you land on any number that hasn't yet been marked? Explain your answer.

3a Use a yellow crayon to color in the multiples of 8 that are *also* multiples of 2 on the Hundreds Grid.

b What do you notice?

2 Circle all of the multiples of 8 on this Hundreds Grid, starting with 8.

1	2	3	4	5	6	7	8	9	10
11	12	13	14	15	16	17	18	19	20
21	22	23	24	25	26	27	28	29	30
31	32	33	34	35	36	37	38	39	40
41	42	43	44	45	46	47	48	49	50
51	52	53	54	55	56	57	58	59	60
61	62	63	64	65	66	67	68	69	70
71	72	73	74	75	76	77	78	79	80
81	82	83	84	85	86	87	88	89	90
91	92	93	94	95	96	97	98	99	100

CHALLENGE

4a Use a red crayon to color in the multiples of 8 that are *also* multiples of 3.

b What do you notice?

Week 2 Discussing the Multiples of 8

Begin the second workout by having students return to page 62 in their Student Books, which they completed last week. Have them briefly discuss, first in pairs and then as a class, their answers to questions 1 and 3 on the sheet. Next, with student input, record the multiples of 8 (up to 96) in a horizontal line along the whiteboard, working near the Number Line if possible so that students can easily refer to it as needed.

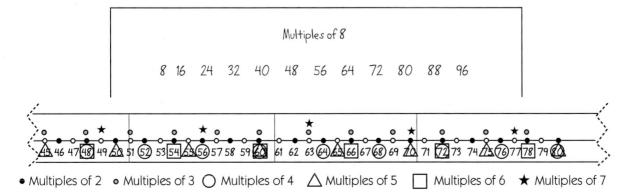

Multiples of 8

8   16   24   32   40   48   56   64   72   80   88   96

• Multiples of 2   ○ Multiples of 3   ○ Multiples of 4   △ Multiples of 5   ▢ Multiples of 6   ★ Multiples of 7

Number Line Multiples of 8 & 9 (cont.)

Ask students to identify any of these 12 numbers that are *also* multiples of 2. How do they know? Circle the multiples of 2 as they name them. As it becomes clear that all of them are multiples of 2, ask students to volunteer explanations for why all of the multiples of 8 are also multiples of 2.

Next, ask students to identify any of the listed numbers that are also multiples of 3. You might remind them that they did this in question 4 last week. If no one had a chance to explore this question the previous week, have them work together to identify the multiples of 3 in the collection on the board, while you underline them. Encourage student pairs to use their calculators to help with this task if necessary.

When all the multiples of 3 have been marked, ask students to share observations.

> **Students** *Every single one is a multiple of 2.*
> *Every third one is also a multiple of 3.*
> *Maybe every fourth one will be a multiple of 4.*
> *But they're all multiples of 4, I think. I know that for sure with 8, 16, 24, 32, and 40.*
> *Let's check out the other ones with our calculators.*

If it doesn't emerge in discussion, ask students to identify the multiples of 8 that are also multiples of 4, 5, and 6. Mark them as they are identified and then ask students to share observations, predictions, and conjectures. Why is every multiple of 8 also a multiple of 2 and 4? Why is every 5th multiple of 8 also a multiple of 5 and every 3rd multiple of 8 also a multiple of 6? Based on their findings so far, what might they predict about multiples of 8 that are also multiples of 7, 9, and 10? Why are things working this way?

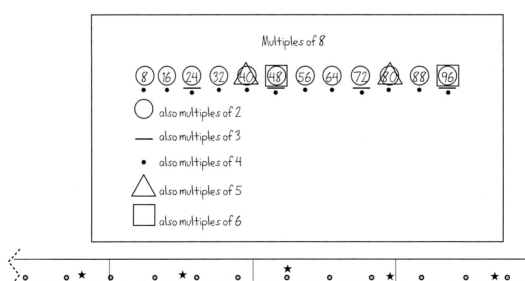

Number Line Multiples of 8 & 9 (cont.)

Weeks 3 & 4 Discussing the Multiples of 9

During your third and fourth Number Line Workouts this month, repeat the steps for weeks 1 and 2 with the multiples of 9, using page 67 in the Number Corner Student Book.

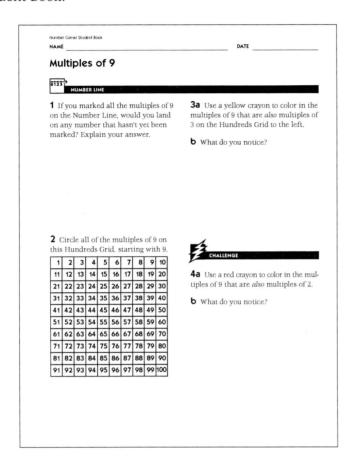

Note If your school year is similar to most, your Number Line will be completely full sometime in February. If your class is interested in continuing to track the number of school days through the rest of the year, you can use Blacklines NC 6.7–6.9 to construct the record sheet shown below, which is partially filled in.

						Days of School Beyond 100														
February	101	102	103	104	105															
March																				
April																				
May																				
June																				

Number Line Multiples of 8 & 9 (cont.)

You might pose specific questions, such as, "During which month will we spend the most days in school between now and June?" You could also let students formulate their own questions that can be answered using the data collected on this record sheet. The record sheet won't be used in future Number Line Workouts, though, so if students are not interested in keeping track of the days of school you do not need to construct it.

February Answer Keys

 ANSWER KEY

Number Corner Student Book

page 61, February Problem Solving Sheet 1

1 9 full rolls (with 25 pennies left over)

2 **a & b** 1 table and 9 stools, 4 tables and 5 stools, 7 tables and 1 stool

Students' methods will vary, and most will employ guess-and-check. However, creating table similar to the one below is one systematic way of finding all the possibilities.

Number of Tables	Number of Legs	31 Legs – Table Legs	Divisible by 3?	If divisible by 3, how many stools?	Solution
1	4	31− 4 = 27	27 ÷ 3 = 9	9	1 table, 9 stools
2	8	31− 8 = 23	no		
3	12	31−12 = 19	no		
4	16	31−16 = 15	15 ÷ 3 = 5	5	4 tables, 5 stools
5	20	31−20 = 11	no		
6	24	31−24 = 7	no		
7	28	31−28 = 3	3 ÷ 3 = 1	1	7 tables, 1 stool

page 62, Multiples of 8

1 If you marked all the multiples of 8, you would not land on any unmarked numbers. Students' explanations will vary. Examples:

example 1: *Because all the multiples of 2 and 4 have been marked already, all of the multiples of 8 have already been marked as well.*

example 2: *All the multiples of 8 are even, and all the multiples of 2 have already been marked. So all the even numbers are already marked.*

2

1	2	3	4	5	6	7	⑧	9	10
11	12	13	14	15	⑯	17	18	19	20
21	22	23	㉔	25	26	27	28	29	30
31	㉜	33	34	35	36	37	38	39	㊵
41	42	43	44	45	46	47	㊽	49	50
51	52	53	54	55	㊶	57	58	59	60
61	62	63	㉞	65	66	67	68	69	70
71	㉢	73	74	75	76	77	78	79	⑧⓪
81	82	83	84	85	86	87	㊴	89	90
91	92	93	94	95	㊺	97	98	99	100

3 **a** All of the multiples of 8 are also multiples of 2.

   b Students' responses will vary. Many may notice that all the multiples of 8 are also multiples of 2.

4 **a** 24, 48, 72, 96 are the multiples of both 8 and 3.

   b Students' responses will vary. Many may notice that every third multiple of 8 is also a multiple of 3 or that all the multiples of 24 are multiples of 3 and 8.

page 63, Roll & Multiply Data Chart

1 The *y*-axis should be labeled something like *Total Products* and the *x*-axis should be labeled with something like *Even* and *Odd*.

2 Students' graphs will vary depending on the data. Be sure students have transferred the data to the graph accurately.

3 Students' responses will vary depending on the data. Be sure that they have interpreted the data correctly. Your data will probably indicate that the probability of getting an odd number is unlikely.

4 Students' responses will vary depending on the data. Be sure that they have interpreted the data correctly. Your data will probably indicate that the probability of getting an even number is likely.

ANSWER KEY

Number Corner Student Book (cont.)

page 64, February Problem Solving Sheet 2

1 **a** $30 \div 6 = 5$ Students' thinking will vary. Most may just recall this fact.

b $300 \div 6 = 50$ Students' thinking will vary. Example:

$30 \div 6 = 5$, so $300 \div 6 = 50$. It's 10 times as much.

c $360 \div 6 = 60$ Students' thinking will vary. Example:

I know $36 \div 6$ is 6, so $360 \div 6$ is 60, because it's 10 times as much.

d $390 \div 6 = 65$ Students' thinking will vary. Example:

I know $360 \div 6$ is 60. And $360 + 30 = 390$. $30 \div 6$ is 5. So $390 \div 6$ is 65, because 390 is 30 more than 360 and $30 \div 6 = 5$.

2 Anne will have to buy 3 dozen eggs. Students' methods will vary. Examples:

example 1:

$2 \times 7 = 14$ eggs for Anne each week

$2 \times 7 = 14$ eggs for the cats each week

6 eggs for the neighbor

Anne needs $14 + 14 + 6 = 34$ eggs

There are 36 eggs in 3 dozen and 24 eggs in 2 dozen. She needs 3 dozen because 2 dozen is not enough.

example 2:

I drew 4 eggs cartons because I thought it would be a lot. Then I colored in Anne's eggs, her cats' eggs, and her neighbor's eggs. It was almost 3 cartons, so she needs 3 dozen eggs.

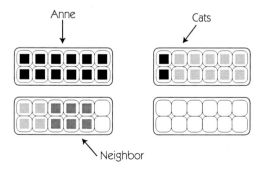

page 65, Thinking about Roll & Multiply

1 Students' observations will vary widely.

2

×	4	5	6	7	8	9
4	16	20	24	28	32	36
5	20	25	30	35	40	45
6	24	30	36	42	48	54
7	28	35	42	49	56	63
8	32	40	48	56	64	72
9	36	45	54	63	72	81

3 **a** There are 36 products on the table.

b 9 of those 36 products are odd.

c The other 27 products are even.

d Students' conclusions will vary, but most will probably note that this tells them that the chance of getting an even product is far higher than the chance of getting an odd product. At this point in the year, some students may express the probability of getting either kind of number numerically: the probability of getting an even product is $^{27}/_{36}$ or $^{3}/_{4}$, and the probability of getting an odd product is $^{9}/_{36}$ or $^{1}/_{4}$.

page 66, February Problem Solving Sheet 3

1 **a** The missing numbers are 12 and 10. The function machine adds 6 to each *in* number to get each *out* number.

b The missing numbers are 24, 54, and 60. The function machine multiplies each *in* number by 6 to get each *out* number.

2 6 math books and 8 dictionaries, Students' methods will vary. Examples:

example 1: *I know that the books could cost $8 each because 48 and 64 are both multiples of 8. So if that is how much they cost, she got 6 math books and 8 dictionaries. $6 + 8$ is 14, and it says she got 14 books altogether, so I know that has to be right.*

ANSWER KEY

Number Corner Student Book (cont.)

page 66, February Problem Solving Sheet 3 (cont.)

2 example 2:

Price of each book	Number of math books	Number of dictionaries	Total books	Right answer?
2	24	32	56	No!
4	12	16	28	No
8	6	8	**14**	Yes

page 67, Multiples of 9

1 If you marked all the multiples of 9, you would not land on any unmarked numbers. Students' explanations will vary. Example:
No, because all the multiples of 9 are also multiples of 3, and the multiples of 3 have already been marked.

2

1	2	3	4	5	6	7	8	9	10
11	12	13	14	15	16	17	18	19	20
21	22	23	24	25	26	27	28	29	30
31	32	33	34	35	36	37	38	39	40
41	42	43	44	45	46	47	48	49	50
51	52	53	54	55	56	57	58	59	60
61	62	63	64	65	66	67	68	69	70
71	72	73	74	75	76	77	78	79	80
81	82	83	84	85	86	87	88	89	90
91	92	93	94	95	96	97	98	99	100

3 **a** All the multiples of 9 are also multiples of 3.
b Students' observations will vary, but most will notice that all the multiples of 9 are also multiples of 3.

4 **a** 18, 36, 54, 72, and 90 are the multiples of 9 and 2.
b Students' observations will vary. Many will notice that every other multiple of 9 is a multiple of 2 as well, or that all the multiples of both 9 and 2 are multiples of 18.

page 68, Extending the Function Machine Pattern

1

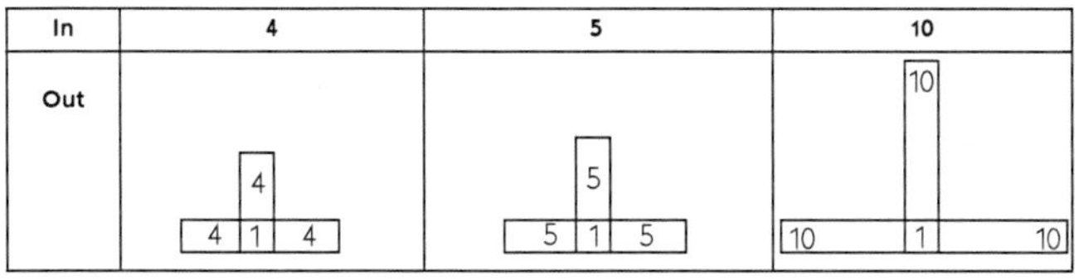

2 For parts a, b, and c, students' equations will vary. One example is provided for each.
a $4 \times 3 + 1 = 12 + 1 = 13$
b $5 \times 3 + 1 = 15 + 1 = 16$
c $10 \times 3 + 1 = 30 + 1 = 31$

3 Students' descriptions will vary.

4 121, because $40 \times 3 + 1 = 120 + 1 = 121$

page 69, One More Look at Roll & Multiply

1 Students' data will depend on your class data. Be sure students have transferred the class data to this chart accurately.

2 **a**

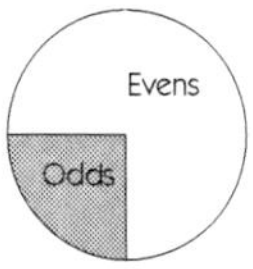

b Students' explanations will vary. Examples:
example 1: *It's a lot more likely that you will get even than odd.*
example 2: *About a fourth of the products were odd and the rest were even. I picked this one because it shows a fourth odd.*
example 3: *I remember on the chart of products that 9 out of 36 were odd and 27 out of 36 were even. That's 1/4 and 3/4, so I picked this one, because it shows 1/4 odd and 3/4 even.*

Number Line

0 1 2 3 4 5 6 7 8 9 10 11 12 13 14 15 16 17 18 19 20 21 22 23 24 25 26 27 28 29 30 31 32 33 34 35 36 37 38 39 40 41 42 43 44 45 46 47 48 49 50 51 52 53 54 55 56 57 58 59

● Multiples of 2   ○ Multiples of 3   △ Multiples of 4   □ Multiples of 5   Multiples of 6   ★ Multiples of 7

Number Corner Student Book
NAME __David__   DATE _____

Quick Facts Tracking Sheet

COMPUTATIONAL FLUENCY

When you get back your Quick Facts Worksheet from last week, look at your score. Record the date you completed the sheet, the time it took you, and the number of facts you got correct in the table below. If it took you more than 2 minutes or you got fewer than 38 facts correct, write "no" in the last column and use that same multiplier again. If you completed 38 or more facts correctly in 1–2 minutes, write "yes" in the last column and choose another multiplier.

Cross out each number as you master the set of facts for that multiplier.

✗ ✗ ✗ ✗ 7 8 9 10 11 12

Multiplier	Date	Time	Number Correct	Mastered? (at least 38 correct in 1–2 minutes)
2	1/12	1–2 min.	39	Yes
5	1/19	1–2 min.	40	Yes
3	1/26	2–3 min.	37	No
3	2/2	1–2 min.	39	Yes
4	2/9	2–3 min.	35	No
4	2/16	1–2 min.	40	Yes
6	2/23	4 min.	39	No
6	3/2	1–2 min.	40	Yes

Computational Fluency

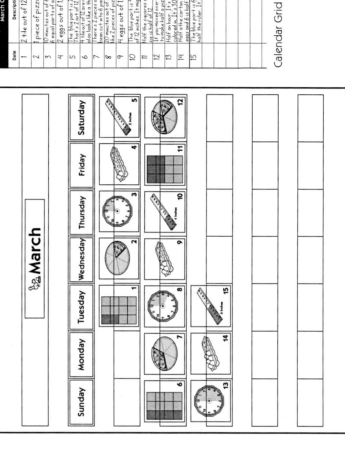

March

Sunday	Monday	Tuesday	Wednesday	Thursday	Friday	Saturday
		1	2	3	4	5
6	7	8	9	10	11	12
13	14	15				

March Calendar Record Sheet

Date	Description of Part and Whole	Fraction
1	2 tile out of 12 are red.	2/12
2	1 piece of pizza out of 6	1/6
3	10 minutes out of 60 colored in, also 1 out of 6 equal parts to a circle colored in.	10/60, 1/6
4	2 eggs out of 12 are in the carton.	2/12
5	The blue part is 2 inches long. That's 2 out of 12 inches	2/12
6	4 tile out of 12 are red. If you blur your eyes, it also looks like a third of the rectangle is red	4/12 or 1/3
7	There's 2 pieces of pizza out of 6 pizza that been cut into 6 parts.	2/6
8	20 minutes out of 60 colored in. It's also like 2 pieces of pizza. It's 1/3 of the clock.	20/60 or 2/6 or 1/3
9	4 eggs out of 12 are in the carton.	4/12
10	The blue part is 4 inches long. That's 4 out of 12 inches. It might be one third of the ruler. six is half of 12	4/12 or 1/3 ?
11	Half the squares are red 6 out of 12 are red	6/12 or 1/2
12	If you moved over 1 piece they'd fit together to make half a pizza. 3 pieces of 6	3/6 or 1/2
13	Half an hour. It's 12:30 Half the circle is colored in. It's 30 minutes out of 60.	1/2 or 30/60
14	Half the carton is filled. That's 6 out of 12 eggs and 6 is half of 12	6/12 or 1/2
15	The blue part is 6 inches long. It's definitely half the ruler. It's 6 out of 12 inches	6/12 or 1/2

Calendar Grid

March

March Problem Solving Sheet 3

PROBLEM SOLVING

1a Color $\frac{1}{2}$ of the squares in this array blue. Color $\frac{1}{4}$ of the squares in this array red. Color $\frac{1}{8}$ of the squares in this array yellow.

b What fraction of the array is left uncolored?

2 Lupe wanted to see which of her three frogs could jump the farthest. She measured their jumps and showed the results on the graph below.

Distance Frogs Jumped

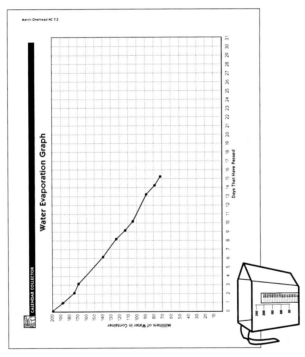

Key: = $3\frac{1}{4}$ inches

a How far did each frog jump?

Junior _____

Frogger _____

DJ _____

b How much farther did DJ jump than Frogger?

Problem Solving

CALENDAR COLLECTOR

Water Evaporation Graph

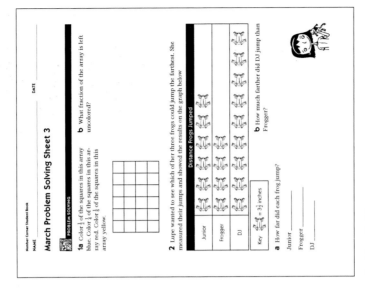

Milliliters of Water in Container

Days That Have Passed

Water Evaporation Record Sheet

Sun.	Mon.	Tues.	Wed.	Thurs.	Fri.	Sat.
			O	X	X	X
	X	X	X	X	X	X
	X	X	X			
	X					

Days That Have Passed	Milliliters of Water
0	200 mL
1 day	188 mL
2 days	176 mL
3 days	170 mL
6 days	140 mL
8 days	125 mL
9 days	115 mL
10 days	108 mL
13 days	90 mL
14 days	80 mL
15 days	73 mL

Calendar Collector

What's Going to Happen in March?

The Number Corner workouts this month spiral back into material that students have already explored this year—prime numbers, division with remainders, multiplication—and press forward into new mathematical territory, including rounding to the nearest tenth, adding fractions with like denominators, and classifying and applying problem-solving strategies.

Calendar Grid

The March calendar pattern features twelfths and sixths shown as parts of a rectangular array, pizza, clock face, egg carton, and ruler. For five days, one-sixth is shown on each model. For the next five days, two-sixths is shown on each model, and so on.

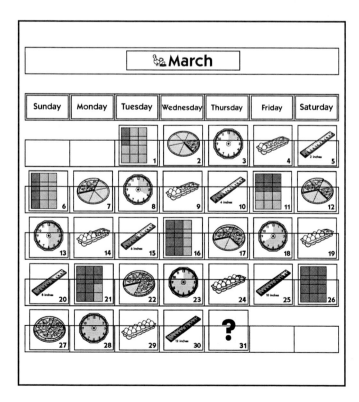

Every five days, the fraction shown on the markers increases by one-sixth, and students are asked to figure out what is similar about each set of five markers. For example, they consider what a rectangular array with 2 red tile out of 12 has in common with a sixth of a pizza. In considering questions like these, students develop deeper understandings of equivalent fractions and intuitive ideas about common denominators.

Calendar Collector

Students collect data from an experiment in which they leave an open measuring cup filled with 200 milliliters of water (about 7 ounces, or a little less than a cup) sitting in a safe place somewhere in the classroom. On each day of school, students record how much water is in the cup. Students will quickly discover (and may have predicted) that the water level is dropping. When they plot the data on a line graph later in the month, they will be able to tell at what rate the level is falling and predict when the cup will be empty. This workout is designed to provide students with experiences setting up and monitoring an experiment, measuring liquid in milliliters, charting change using a line graph, and reading and interpreting line graphs.

	Sun.	Mon.	Tues.	Wed.	Thurs.	Fri.	Sat.
			O	X	X	X	X
	X	X					

Water Evaporation Record Sheet	
Days That Have Passed	Milliliters of Water
0	200 mL
1 day	188 mL
2 days	176 mL
3 days	170 mL
6 days	140 mL

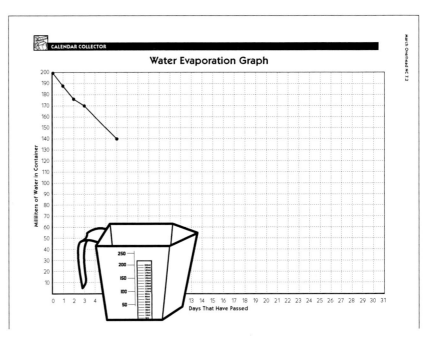

Computational Fluency

Students continue with the Quick Facts routine from March and February. Each week, students work with one multiplier of their choice until they can complete at least 38 facts for that multiplier correctly in 2 minutes or less. When they can, they move on to a new multiplier of their choice, with the ultimate goal of mastering the facts for all multipliers from 2 to 12.

Problem Solving

Each Problem Solving page this month offers two complex, multi-step problems, many of which involve computation in the context of reading and interpreting graphs or tables. Three of the problems involve fractions, thereby reinforcing and extending students' work with fractions on the Calendar Grid.

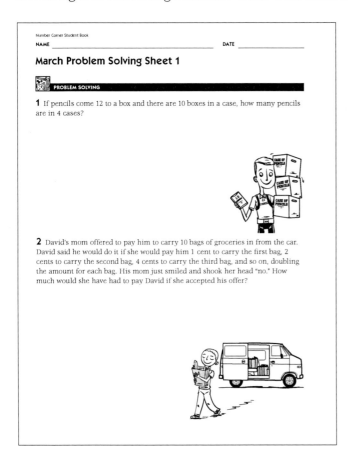

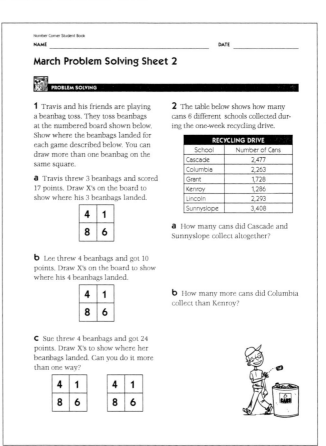

In many districts, students are expected to understand and use specific strategies for solving problems, the most common of which are listed below. Students will generate many of these strategies on their own if given time and the appropriate materials. However, guidance is offered this month for introducing and helping students to classify these strategies as needed.

- acting out the situation or using objects
- making a sketch or a picture
- using or looking for a pattern
- making an organized list
- using or making a table or a chart
- using logical reasoning—working from things they know to things they don't know
- guess and check

Number Line

This month, students examine the numbers that never got marked on the Number Line, in other words, the numbers that were not identified as multiples of 2, 3, 4, 5, 6, 7, 8, or 9. During this exploration, students revisit the concepts of prime and composite numbers, factors, and multiples. Later in the month, a new version of the familiar game of Round & Add is introduced. In it, students round decimal numbers between 0 and 1 to the nearest tenth on a number line. In this version of the game, the team whose actual and rounded totals match most closely wins.

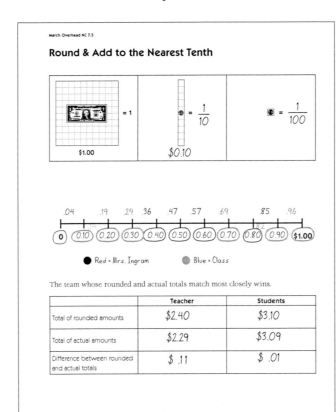

Assessment & Support Activities

This month includes the third of four quarterly basic skills checkups. The March checkup focuses on basic multiplication and division facts; multi-digit addition and subtraction in the context of story problems; 1-digit by 2-digit multiplication in the context of reading and interpreting a pictograph; filling in values to create equations that are true; calculating area and perimeter; reading and interpreting a bar graph; identifying the probability of a specific event; and identifying and modeling common fractions. This checkup, like the other three checkups this year, is optional. However, we find it provides a good summary of what students know and can do with regard to basic or "life-skills" math at this point in the school year, and also provides an opportunity to practice test-taking skills.

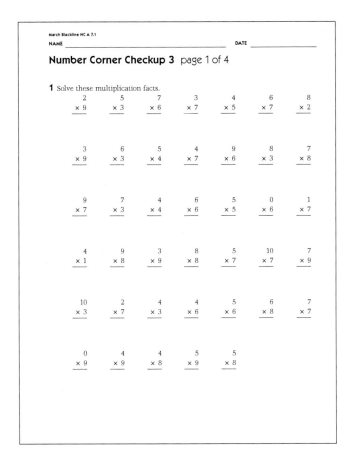

NAME _____ DATE _____

Number Corner Checkup 3 page 1 of 4

1 Solve these multiplication facts.

2	5	7	3	4	6	8
× 9	× 3	× 6	× 7	× 5	× 7	× 2

3	6	5	4	9	8	7
× 9	× 3	× 4	× 7	× 6	× 3	× 8

9	7	4	6	5	0	1
× 7	× 3	× 4	× 6	× 5	× 6	× 7

4	9	3	8	5	10	7
× 1	× 8	× 9	× 8	× 7	× 7	× 9

10	2	4	4	5	6	7
× 3	× 7	× 3	× 6	× 6	× 8	× 7

0	4	4	5	5
× 9	× 9	× 8	× 9	× 8

NAME _____ DATE _____

Number Corner Checkup 3 page 2 of 4

2 Solve these division facts.

$8\overline{)24}$ $3\overline{)15}$ $5\overline{)20}$ $4\overline{)16}$ $5\overline{)45}$ $1\overline{)12}$ $4\overline{)32}$

$6\overline{)36}$ $4\overline{)40}$ $3\overline{)27}$ $3\overline{)21}$ $8\overline{)32}$ $7\overline{)14}$ $3\overline{)18}$

3 The school cafeteria at Carus Elementary served 3,457 slices of pizza last year and 2,984 slices of pizza this year.

a How many total slices of pizza did the cafeteria serve in these 2 years?

b How many more slices of pizza did they serve last year than this year?

4 The fourth-graders at Shoreham Elementary decided to keep track of the number of pizza slices sold each month in the cafeteria. The graph below shows their findings for the first 4 months of the year. Fill in the box at the end of each row to show how many pieces the cafeteria sold each month.

Slices of Pizza Sold Each Month		
Month	Pizza Slices Sold	Total for the Month
a January	🍕🍕🍕🍕🍕🍕	
b February	🍕🍕🍕🍕	
c March	🍕🍕🍕🍕🍕🍕🍕	
d April	🍕🍕🍕	

Key 🍕 = 24 slices

We suggest that you administer the checkup at the end of the month, or even very early in April, as it may provide information that is timely and useful to you in writing third-quarter report cards. After reviewing students' responses to the items on the checkup, you can assign Support Activities as needed for children to work on at school or at home. At the end of the assessment write-up, we have recommended specific activities that may be helpful. You'll find all Support Activities in their own section at the end of the Number Corner Blacklines.

Planning for March

You can use the planning guide below as shown or adapt it to fit the needs of your students and schedule. If you like, you can use it along with the week-by-week write-ups to fill in a day-by-day planner for the month using Blackline NC 1.1.

MARCH PLANNING GUIDE	MON	TUES	WED	THURS	FRI	SB
Key ★ = Discuss ☆ = Update SB = Number Corner Student Book						
Calendar Grid, pp. 265–270 Equivalent Fractions • modeling, recognizing, and comparing common fractions • exploring equivalent fractions and using equivalence to compare fractions	★	☆	☆	☆	★	pp. 74 & 76
Calendar Collector, pp.271–275 The Water Evaporation Experiment • conducting experiments; systematically collecting and recording data; drawing, supporting, and communicating conclusions based on data collected • accurately measuring capacity to the nearest milliliter • reading, interpreting, and constructing line graphs	☆	★	☆	☆	☆	pp. 72 & 77
Computational Fluency, pp.276–279 Quick Facts • fluently using multiplication facts through 12 x 12 • developing efficient strategies for solving basic division fact			★			p. 50
Problem Solving, pp. 280–283 Graphs, Tables & Fractions • modeling, adding, and subtracting commonly used fractions • adding and subtracting up to 4-digit numbers with and without regrouping • multiplying 2- and 3-digit numbers by 1-digit numbers • reading and interpreting a bar graph, pictograph, and table				★		pp. 70, 73, 75 & 78
Number Line, pp. 284–288 Prime Numbers & Round & Add to the Nearest Tenth • exploring concepts of prime and composite numbers, factors, and multiples • modeling, recognizing, ordering, adding, and rounding decimals to the nearest tenth	☆	☆	☆	☆	★	p. 71
Assessment, pp. 289–291 Number Corner Checkup 3	Give this assessment during the last week of March or first week of April. (Blacklines NC A 7.1–7.4)					
Support Activities, pp. 291 and 292 Multi-Digit Addition & Subtraction, Perimeter, Multiplication & Division, Fractions	Use after Number Corner Checkup 3. (Blacklines NC S 12.1–25.6)					

Materials You'll Need for March

MANIPULATIVES & MATERIALS

Manipulatives
- Calendar Grid pocket chart
- 1 pair of dice numbered 1–6 for each pair of students
- 2 dice, one marked 1–6 and one marked 4–9
- game markers
- calculators (optional)
- overhead money value pieces
- half-class set of base ten pieces (optional, Use Blackline NC 1.9 if needed.)
- colored tile or 1˝ × 1˝ tag board or construction paper squares in red, blue, and yellow (optional)
- 1-cup liquid measuring cup

Number Corner Calendar Markers
- Day, Month, and Year markers
- Equivalent Fraction calendar markers

Number Corner Components
- Number Line

General Materials
- rulers
- overhead pens in red and blue
- crayons
- piece of paper to mask parts of the overhead when necessary
- a few blank overhead transparencies
- pointer (such as a yard or meter stick)
- piece of chart paper

BLACKLINES & OVERHEADS

Number Corner Overheads
NC 5.1	Quick Facts Worksheet
NC 5.2	Quick Facts Tracking Sheet
NC 7.1	March Problem Solving Sheet 1
NC 7.2	Water Evaporation Graph
NC 7.3	March Problem Solving Sheet 2
NC 7.4	March Problem Solving Sheet 3
NC 7.5	Round It to the Nearest Tenth
NC 7.6	March Problem Solving Sheet 4

Number Corner Blacklines
NC 1.1	Monthly Planner Template (1 copy, optional)
NC 1.9	Base Ten Pieces (create your own half-class set of base ten pieces if needed)
NC 5.5	Multiplication Facts Class Checklist (1 or 2 copies saved from January, optional)
NC 5.6	Quick Facts Worksheet (4 class sets)
NC 6.5	Problem Solving Solution Page (class set, optional)
NC 7.1 & 7.2	March Calendar Grid Record Sheet, pages 1 and 2 (1 copy each)
NC 7.3 & 7.4	Water Evaporation Record Sheet, pages 1 and 2 (1 copy each)
NC 7.5	Measuring Cup Calibration Strip (1 copy)
NC 7.6	March Problem Strips (class set, optional)

Number Corner Assessment Blacklines
NC A 7.1–7.4	Number Corner Checkup 3, pages 1–4
NC A 7.5–7.7	Number Corner Checkup 3 Class Checklist, pages 1–3 (2 or 3 copies as needed, optional)

Number Corner Student Book
page 50	Quick Facts Tracking Sheet
page 70	March Problem Solving Sheet 1
page 71	Multiples on the Number Line
page 72	Water Evaporation Graph
page 73	March Problem Solving Sheet 2
page 74	A Closer Look at the Fractions Pattern
page 75	March Problem Solving Sheet 3
page 76	More About Fractions
page 77	Looking at Line Graphs
page 78	March Problem Solving Sheet 4

Materials You'll Need for March (cont.)

ADVANCE PREPARATION

Calendar Grid

Run 1 copy each of Blacklines NC 7.1 and 7.2. Trim and then glue or tape them together to form one long chart. Post on your calendar display board before you conduct your first Calendar Grid Workout this month.

Calendar Collector

Run 1 copy each of Blacklines NC 7.3 and 7.4. Trim and then glue or tape them together to form one long chart. Post on your calendar display board before you conduct your first Calendar Collector Workout this month.

You'll also need to use the Calibration Strip (Blackline 7.5) to calibrate the measuring cup that was supplied with your Number Corner materials. Run a single copy of the blackline and follow the directions on the sheet. Be sure to use this container. A graduated cylinder, for example, will not expose enough water to the air, so the water will evaporate too slowly.

Number Line

If you have not already done so, mark the multiples of 8 and 9 on the Number Line before the first workout this month.

March Calendar Grid

CALENDAR GRID

Equivalent Fractions

STUDENT BOOK

Overview

The March Calendar Grid pattern features twelfths and sixths shown as parts of a rectangular array, pizza, clock face, egg carton, and ruler. Students are challenged to find similarities between the markers by answering questions such as, "What does a rectangular array with 2 red tile out of 12 have in common with a sixth of a pizza, 10 minutes on a clock, 2 eggs in a carton that holds 12, and 2 inches on a ruler?"

Frequency

Update the Calendar Grid and record sheet each day and share observations and predictions at least once a week.

Skills & Concepts

★ modeling, recognizing, and comparing common fractions

★ using a variety of visual models to conceptualize fractions and interpret different meanings for fractions

★ exploring equivalent fractions and using equivalence to compare fractions

★ adding commonly used fractions using visual representations

★ describing, extending, and making verbal and written generalizations about patterns

★ extending number patterns that grow by common differences

You'll need

★ March Calendar Grid Record Sheet, pages 1 and 2 (Blacklines NC 7.1 and 7.2, see Advance Preparation)

★ A Closer Look at the Fractions Pattern (Number Corner Student Book, page 74)

★ More About Fractions (Number Corner Student Book, page 76)

★ Calendar Grid pocket chart

★ Day, Month, and Year markers

★ Equivalent Fraction calendar markers

Advance Preparation Run 1 copy each of Blacklines NC 7.1 and 7.2. Trim and then glue or tape them together to form one long chart. Post on your calendar display board before you conduct your first Calendar Grid Workout this month.

Week 1 Introducing & Discussing the First Two Markers

Open your first Calendar Grid Workout this month by placing the first two markers in the Calendar Grid pocket chart.

Calendar Grid Equivalent Fractions (cont.)

Ask students to converse in pairs and then share observations with the whole group. You can ask one or more of the following questions to get them started.

• What do you notice about these two markers?
• What is different about the two markers and what is the same?
• How do the two markers relate to one another? What does a rectangular array in which 2 of the 12 tile are red have to do with a slice of pizza? (Although the observation that 10 out of 12 tile are blue is equally important, ask students to focus on the red tile this month.)

Spend the majority of the workout having students share observations and comparisons, and then, with student input, complete the first two entries on the March Calendar Grid Record Sheet. If you start later than the second of the month, post additional calendar markers and add their information on to the record sheet.

March Calendar Record Sheet		
Date	Description of Part and Whole	Fraction
1	2 tile out of 12 are red.	$\frac{2}{12}$
2	1 piece of pizza out of 6	$\frac{1}{6}$

Week 2 Making Predictions about the 8th or 9th Marker

Open the second workout by asking students to discuss and predict, first in pairs and then as a whole group, what the marker for today (or tomorrow if today's marker has already been posted) will look like. As they share their predictions, ask them to explain their thinking. In doing so, students are likely to share a variety of ways to name and compare the fractions, which is to be encouraged.

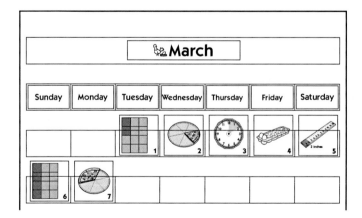

Students *The next marker will have an 8 on it for sure.*
It'll also have a clock, because the pattern is going tiles, pizza, clock, eggs, ruler. Then it starts again with the tiles and the pizza, so it'll be a clock next.

Calendar Grid Equivalent Fractions (cont.)

The clock will have more yellow on it, because there are more red tiles on the second rectangle and another piece of pizza in the second pan.

I think the clock is kind of like the pizza. The yellow part is like a piece of pizza.

The first yellow part was 10 minutes, so maybe it'll add on another 10 minutes on this next marker.

I agree. I think it'll say 12:20. Twenty minutes is $^1/_3$ of an hour. I remember from the clocks in March.

And if you squint up your eyes, the red tiles on marker 6 take up $^1/_3$ of that rectangle.

I think all of these next markers are going to be like thirds.

After students have had opportunities to share their predictions, post the next marker and take time with the class to update the record sheet.

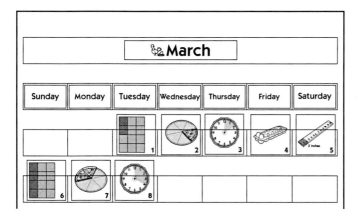

March Calendar Record Sheet		
Date	Description of Part and Whole	Fraction
1	2 tile out of 12 are red.	$\frac{2}{12}$
2	1 piece of pizza out of 6	$\frac{1}{6}$
3	10 minutes out of 60 colored in; also 1 out of 6 equal parts of a circle colored in.	$\frac{10}{60}$ or $\frac{1}{6}$
4	2 eggs of 12 are in the carton.	$\frac{2}{12}$
5	The blue part is 2 inches long. That's 2 out of 12 inches.	$\frac{2}{12}$
6	4 tile out of 12 are red. If you blur yours eyes, it also looks like a third of the rectangle is red.	$\frac{4}{12}$ or $\frac{1}{3}$
7	There's 2 pieces of pizza out of a pizza that been cut into 6 parts.	$\frac{2}{6}$
8	20 minutes out of 60 colored in. It's also like 2 pieces of pizza. It's $\frac{1}{3}$ of the clock.	$\frac{20}{60}$ or $\frac{2}{6}$ or $\frac{1}{3}$

Note *In the event that some students have difficulty moving beyond the repeating pattern of the 5 different models (i.e., tile, pizza, clock, egg carton, ruler), you may find it helpful to discuss the difference between students' thinking about patterns in earlier grades and this pattern. When they were younger, it was an accomplishment to predict the sequence of pictures. Fourth graders pick up on the picture patterns much more quickly, however, and the real learning goal revolves around understanding what is happening with the fractions represented by these models.*

Week 3 Making Observations & Predictions

Open your third workout by having students work in pairs to complete Student Book page 74. The purpose of this sheet is to give students an opportunity to study the calendar markers more closely and to record as many observations about the pattern as they can. You might help students focus by encouraging them to look for likenesses and differences between the markers, and to think in terms of fractions. Emphasize that while they can work

Calendar Grid Equivalent Fractions (cont.)

in pairs and talk to their tablemates, each student should complete his or her own sheet.

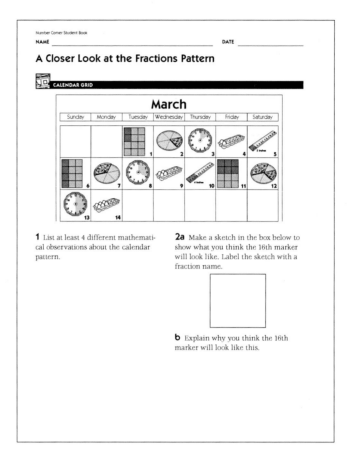

It will take most, if not all, of today's Number Corner period for students to complete this page. If you can, extend today's period or take some time tomorrow to have each pair share one observation about the pattern. Challenge them to make it all the way around the room without repeating any observation. As they share their ideas, you may find that some students have focused on what is empty or not colored in on each marker. This is a perfectly valid way to interpret this month's calendar pattern. If you have time, students can share additional observations after each pair has shared one idea.

You may want to collect students' papers to see how they responded to item 2, which asks them to make a labeled sketch of what they think the 16th marker will look like. Even if a student cannot name the correct fraction, she might be able to draw it. If the student labels her sketch with a fraction, make note of whether the picture and symbolic notation match. You may also find it interesting to see how students explain their predictions at this point in the year.

If you find that some students could benefit from an additional challenge, pose the following questions for them. You may also want to pose these or similar questions to the entire class.

Calendar Grid Equivalent Fractions (cont.)

- What decimal number is equal to the fraction shown on marker 14? How do you know?
- If you add the fractions shown on markers 7 and 12, what fraction would you get? (When asking students to add fractions, be sure to select fractions based on the same model to ensure that the whole is consistent.) Write an equation to show these fractions and their sum.

Week 4 Thinking about Thirds

In the fourth workout, have students complete Student Book page 76, which asks them to make connections between 5 markers that all show ¹/₃ on a different model. Have students work together as a class to generate two fraction names for the first marker. Then ask them to complete the rest of the page independently or in pairs if they prefer to work with someone.

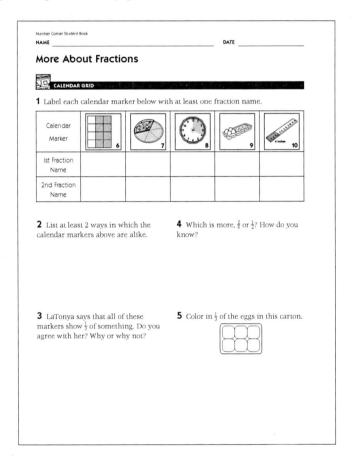

When students have completed the page, you may want to collect their work and look it over later. Their responses to the items on the page will provide a good deal of information regarding their current understandings of fractions. In the last few minutes of the period, invite students to discuss the pattern on the Calendar Grid. What do they notice? Have their predictions about the pattern been confirmed?

Calendar Grid Equivalent Fractions (cont.)

If students need an additional challenge, pose problems similar to those below to small groups of students or to the entire class.

- What decimal number is equal to the fraction shown on marker 28? How do you know?
- What is the sum of the fractions shown on markers 12 and 22? Show the fractions and their sum as an equation.
- What is the difference between the fractions shown on markers 7 and 22? Show the fractions and their difference as an equation.

The 31st calendar marker this month shows a question mark, inviting students to think of their own extensions to this pattern. The fractions have grown by $2/12$ or $1/6$ every 5 markers, so by March 30th, students have seen different models and considered fractions all the way from $2/12$ to $12/12$; $1/6$ to $6/6$; and $10/60$ to $60/60$. What's next? How would this pattern continue if the month of March lasted another several weeks?

March Calendar Collector

CALENDAR COLLECTOR

The Water Evaporation Experiment

STUDENT
BOOK

Overview

Students collect data from a simple experiment in which an open measuring cup filled with 200 milliliters of water is left sitting in a safe place somewhere in the classroom. Each day, students read the water level and record it. Twice this month, students graph the data to see what is happening to the water and to make predictions about what the water levels will be in the days to come.

Frequency

Update the data daily, and share observations and predictions about the data as a whole group once or twice a week.

Skills & Concepts

★ exploring situations that demonstrate varying rates of change

★ conducting experiments; systematically collecting and recording data; drawing, supporting, and communicating conclusions based on data collected

★ accurately measuring capacity to the nearest milliliter

★ reading, interpreting, and constructing line graphs

★ identifying or describing a situation that may be modeled by a given graph

You'll need

★ Water Evaporation Graph (Overhead NC 7.2)

★ Water Evaporation Record Sheet, pages 1 and 2 (Blacklines NC 7.3 and 7.4, 1 copy each, see Advance Preparation)

★ Measuring Cup Calibration Strip (Blackline NC 7.5, 1 copy)

★ Water Evaporation Graph (Number Corner Student Book, page 72)

★ Looking at Line Graphs (Number Corner Student Book, page 77)

★ 1-cup liquid measuring cup calibrated in increments of 10 milliliters (see Advance Preparation)

★ rulers

★ overhead pens

....

Advance Preparation Run 1 copy each of Blacklines NC 7.3 and 7.4. Trim and then glue or tape them together to form one long chart. Post on your calendar display board before you conduct your first Calendar Collector Workout this month.

You'll also need to use the Calibration Strip (Blackline 7.5) to calibrate the measuring cup that was supplied with your Number Corner materials. Run a single copy of the blackline and follow the directions on the sheet. Be sure to use this container. A graduated cylinder, for example, will not expose enough water to the air, so the water will evaporate too slowly.

....

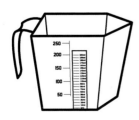

Calendar Collector The Water Evaporation Experiment (cont.)

Week 1 Introducing the Water Evaporation Experiment

Introduce this month's experiment by showing students the calibrated measuring cup. Pass the cup to a student volunteer and ask her to find the mark on the cup that shows 200 milliliters. How does this mark compare with the mark on the other side that shows 1 cup? (Although used as a unit of liquid measure in science laboratories around the world, milliliters are likely to be unfamiliar to most of your students, and it helps them to see that 200 milliliters is a little less than 1 cup, while the 250 milliliter mark near the very top of the measuring cup is just a little over 1 cup.)

Next, ask students to think about what would happen if you filled the cup with water to the 200 milliliter mark and left it sitting somewhere in your classroom *out of direct sunlight*, in a place where it wouldn't get knocked over or disturbed in any way. Students' predictions are sure to vary, but someone will almost certainly suggest that the water will dry up and eventually disappear. If so, ask students about how long they think this will take. Will it happen overnight, in a week, in a month, or longer? Do they think the water will evaporate at a steady rate of x milliliters a day, or more some days than others? Encourage them to explain their hypotheses as thoroughly as they can. If no one suggests that the water will evaporate, accept any predictions students do make and leave the question open.

After the initial discussion, have students help you set up the experiment. Ask a volunteer to carefully fill the cup to the 200 milliliter line, and have another student or two check the measurement for accuracy. They will quickly discover that the cup must be placed on a level surface to take an accurate measurement. Then ask students to help you decide where to place the cup in the classroom.

Once the cup has been set in its location, show students the Water Evaporation Record Sheet. Point out that the initial entry under "Days That Have Passed" is 0 and ask them to explain why it is 0 and not 1. You can use the abbreviation ml or mL for milliliters.

Calendar Collector The Water Evaporation Experiment (cont.)

Finally, explain that a different student helper will read the water level each day and record the measurement on the class record sheet. Emphasize that they should take care to read the number of milliliters carefully and record the number of days that have passed accurately. Students won't be able to take readings on weekends and holidays, so if you start the experiment on Tuesday, for example, and take readings on Wednesday, Thursday, Friday, and then again on Monday, 6 days will have passed on Monday, although it will only be the fourth reading. A miniature calendar is included at the top of the record sheet to help students keep track of how many days have passed. Mark the starting day with a 0 and each successive day with an X.

Weeks 2 & 3 Graphing the Data Collected So Far

For both of these workouts, wait until *after* the class has graphed the data to have a student volunteer take a reading and enter the day's data.

To open the second workout, display a copy of the Water Evaporation Graph overhead and have students turn to page 72 in their Student Books, which features the same graph. Give students a couple of minutes to share observations about the graph. Explain that they will enter a point on the graph for each day a reading has been taken to create a *line graph*, a type of graph commonly used to show changes over time. Then have a student volunteer read out the values that have been entered on the record sheet so far. Record them one by one on your graph as the students do so on theirs. You and the students may find it helpful to use a ruler or the corner of a piece of paper to make sure you are entering the values on the correct days, as well as to connect the dots once all the values have been entered. Be sure everyone understands that you can't make a dot for days on which they didn't take a measurement. The beauty of a line graph is that one can connect the dots to get some idea of what happened on the days when the class was unable to take a reading.

Calendar Collector The Water Evaporation Experiment (cont.)

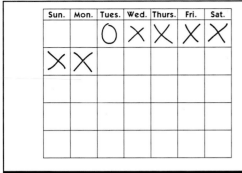

	Sun.	Mon.	Tues.	Wed.	Thurs.	Fri.	Sat.
			O	X	X	X	X
	X	X					

Water Evaporation Record Sheet

Days That Have Passed	Milliliters of Water
0	200 mL
1 day	188 mL
2 days	176 mL
3 days	170 mL
6 days	140 mL

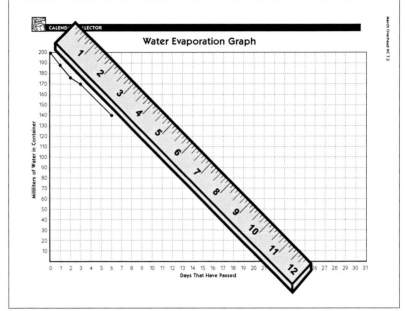

After the data has been entered, give students a few minutes to discuss the results so far. You can ask some of the following questions to help focus the discussion.

- What has happened to the water since you started the experiment?
- How do the results so far match the predictions you made last week?
- What can you say about the rate at which the water is evaporating? How much water has evaporated each day? Is it the same or different each day? If the amount that has evaporated each day is different, are the differences large or small?
- Based on the data, what do you predict for today's reading? (After students have shared their predictions, have a helper read the current water level. Add this value to the class record sheet and have students enter it on their graphs.)
- Based on the data, how many days do you predict it will take for the water to evaporate completely? (You might show students how to use a ruler to extend the line in order to make predictions, as shown above.)

> **Students** It looks like we'll run out of water by about the twentieth day. It'll be gone before Spring Break, I bet.
> I thought it would dry up faster than that.
> I thought it would just stay the same, but it's evaporating pretty quickly.
> It's already gone from 200 to 140 milliliters. That's a lot!

Repeat this process during the third Calendar Collector Workout, graphing the additional data that has been collected and having students share their observations and predictions. Another question to pose during the third workout is: *How might the shape of the data (i.e., the slope of the line) change if we repeated the experiment but put the cup in a different location in the classroom, such as a windowsill that gets plenty of direct sunlight each day or in a dark closet?*

Calendar Collector The Water Evaporation Experiment (cont.)

If student interest in this experiment has been particularly high and you find that the topic of evaporation connects well with your science curriculum, you might repeat the experiment, changing one variable each time (e.g., exposure to sunlight, proximity to heater, partial coverage with plastic wrap, etc.) to explore some of the factors that influence the rate of evaporation.

Week 4 Looking at Line Graphs

The rate at which the water evaporates will vary from classroom to classroom, depending on a number of variables, including room temperature and humidity. In our classroom, it took 28 days for the water to evaporate completely. Depending on the timing of Spring Break, you may not be able to see the experiment through to the end. Either way, students will still have had the benefit of constructing and reading line graphs and experiencing the power they have to help people picture data and make predictions. Build on this experience by having students complete page 77 in the Student Book, which asks them to match four situations involving change over time to the line graphs that best represent them.

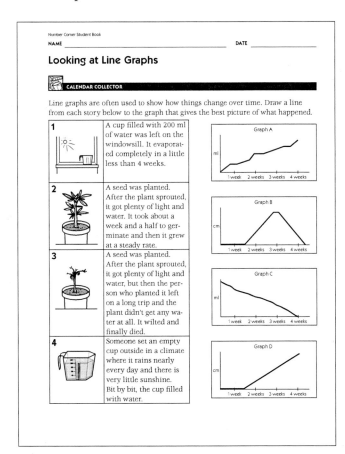

March Computational Fluency

COMPUTATIONAL FLUENCY

STUDENT
BOOK

Quick Facts

Overview

Students continue the Quick Facts routine introduced in January. Students choose their own multipliers, which they'll work with until they can complete 40 facts correctly in 2 minutes or less. Each time they reach that level of fluency, they'll choose another multiplier, working toward the goal of mastering their multiplication facts through 12 × 12 (or 10 × 10 depending on your state standards).

Frequency

One day per week

Skills & Concepts

★ fluently using multiplication facts through 12 × 12

★ developing efficient strategies for solving basic division facts

★ relating multiplication and division

You'll need

★ Quick Facts Worksheet (Overhead NC 5.1)

★ Quick Facts Tracking Sheet (Overhead NC 5.2)

★ Multiplication Facts Class Checklist (Blackline NC 5.5, 1 or 2 copies saved from January, optional)

★ Quick Facts Worksheet (Blackline NC 5.6, 4 class sets)

★ Quick Facts Tracking Sheet (Number Corner Student Book, page 50)

★ 1 pair of dice numbered 1–6 for each pair of students

At the start of each workout, return students' corrected Quick Facts Worksheets from the previous week and have them enter the information on their Quick Facts Tracking Sheet (page 50 in their Student Books). If they completed at least 38 of the 40 facts correctly in 2 minutes or less, they can move along to another multiplier. If not, they'll need to use the same multiplier this week.

Computational Fluency Quick Facts (cont.)

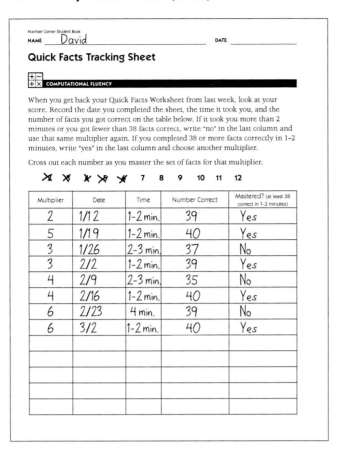

Number Corner Student Book

NAME ___David___ DATE _____

Quick Facts Tracking Sheet

```
+ -
+ ×  COMPUTATIONAL FLUENCY
```

When you get back your Quick Facts Worksheet from last week, look at your score. Record the date you completed the sheet, the time it took you, and the number of facts you got correct on the table below. If it took you more than 2 minutes or you got fewer than 38 facts correct, write "no" in the last column and use that same multiplier again. If you completed 38 or more facts correctly in 1–2 minutes, write "yes" in the last column and choose another multiplier.

Cross out each number as you master the set of facts for that multiplier.

~~2~~ ~~3~~ ~~4~~ ~~5~~ ~~6~~ 7 8 9 10 11 12

Multiplier	Date	Time	Number Correct	Mastered? (at least 38 correct in 1–2 minutes)
2	1/12	1–2 min.	39	Yes
5	1/19	1–2 min.	40	Yes
3	1/26	2–3 min.	37	No
3	2/2	1–2 min.	39	Yes
4	2/9	2–3 min.	35	No
4	2/16	1–2 min.	40	Yes
6	2/23	4 min.	39	No
6	3/2	1–2 min.	40	Yes

After they have recorded the results of the previous week's Quick Facts exercise, give students about 5 minutes to practice their chosen set of facts before starting the worksheet. There are many quick and simple ways to do this. Here are just a few ideas:

- Have students write their own set of flashcards on the spot and then "test" each other.
- Give each pair of students 2 dice numbered 1–6. Have them announce their multipliers to each other and then take turns rolling the 2 dice, adding the 2 numbers, and multiplying the sum by their multiplier.
- Have students list the facts for their multiplier several times on a piece of paper.
- If your classroom is equipped with computers, students can play a quick multiplication practice game electronically.

After they have had a few minutes to practice, reconvene the class and distribute copies of the Quick Facts Worksheet. Have students record their names, the date, and their multiplier before they begin. Then write "0–1" on the board, give the signal to start, and let students go to work as quickly and accurately as they can while you watch the clock. After a minute has passed, write "1–2" on the board. After 2 minutes have passed, record "2–3." After 3 minutes have passed, write "3–4," and after 4 minutes have passed, call time.

Computational Fluency Quick Facts (cont.)

As soon as they have completed the 40 facts, students should turn their paper over, look up at the board, and record the range of time in which they completed the facts. If they have not completed the 40 problems when time is called, ask them to stop, even if they're not finished, and write a 4 in the appropriate space at the top of the sheet.

Finally, have them complete the bottom section of the Quick Facts sheet by choosing 10 different products from the grid above, entering each in one of the dividend boxes, and then dividing each by the multiplier.

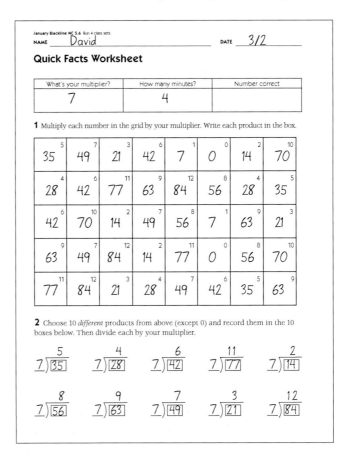

As students finish, collect their papers and remind the class that you'll return the sheets the following week, corrected and ready to be entered on their Quick Facts Tracking Sheet. You can continue to use the Multiplication Facts Class Checklist to keep track of students' progress individually and as a class.

CHALLENGE

If you find that some students know all their facts, give them alternate tasks during this workout for the next couple of months. They might serve as tutors for students who are having a difficult time, or they might work independently on some of the problems from the Problem Solving Workout. Another

Computational Fluency Quick Facts (cont.)

option is to have them play Roll 5, a game that uses all 4 operations and is nearly unlimited in terms of challenge level. The instructions and several copies of the record sheet for this game can be found in the Number Corner Student Book, pages 51–54. You might also have them complete a page of mixed facts. Some students who are fluent with groups of facts may still struggle a bit to complete a set of mixed facts quickly. You can have them use Blackline NC A 7.1 or make your own pages of mixed facts.

 SUPPORT

While we want all fourth graders to be fluent with their multiplication facts by the end of the school year, some students will not reach this goal without considerable support. If some students are still working with 2's, 3's, 5's, or 10's, and struggling to do so, you may want to have them play some of the support games listed after the January Number Corner Checkup with a paraprofessional, resource room teacher, or parent. If a large portion of your class is struggling with the same group or groups of facts, you might select Support Activities for use with the whole class. There are also many engaging software programs designed to help students practice basic facts, and you can certainly give students copies of the Quick Facts sheets to use for home practice during the week as well.

March Problem Solving

PROBLEM SOLVING

STUDENT BOOK

Graphs, Tables & Fractions

Overview

The Problem Solving Workouts offer two new complex, multi-step problems each week. Many of the problems involve computation in the context of reading and interpreting graphs or tables, while others reinforce and extend the work students will be doing with fractions on the Calendar Grid.

Frequency

One day per week

Skills & Concepts

★ using a variety of visual models to conceptualize fractions

★ interpreting fractions as equal parts of a unit whole and parts of a set

★ adding and subtracting commonly used fractions

★ adding and subtracting up to 4-digit numbers with and without regrouping

★ multiplying 2- and 3-digit numbers by 1-digit numbers

★ extending a number pattern that doubles

★ reading and interpreting a bar graph, pictograph, and table

★ selecting methods and tools appropriate to a particular context for operations with whole numbers

★ solving multi-step story problems using a variety of efficient paper/pencil and mental strategies

You'll need

★ March Problem Solving Sheets 1–4 (Overheads NC 7.1, 7.3, 7.4, and 7.6)

★ Problem Solving Solution Page (Blackline NC 6.5, class set, optional)

★ March Problem Strips (Blackline NC 7.6, class set, optional)

★ March Problem Solving Sheets 1–4 (Number Corner Student Book, pages 70, 73, 75, and 78)

★ half-class set of base ten pieces (Use Blackline NC 1.9 to create your own base ten pieces if needed.)

★ game markers

★ calculators (optional)

★ colored tile or 1" x 1" tag board or construction paper squares in red, blue, and yellow (optional)

★ piece of paper to mask parts of the overhead when necessary

★ overhead pens

★ a few blank overhead transparencies

Problem Solving Graphs, Tables & Fractions (cont.)

Each week, ask students to select the one problem on the day's page that appeals to them most. If they have time, they can attempt both, but these problems are complex enough that many students will spend a full Number Corner period on a single problem. Invite students to work alone or in pairs, but make sure they understand that they must record their work on their own sheets. For the first pair of problems, you might have students use the March Problem Strips and a Problem Solving Solution Page to structure their solutions.

Make a variety of tools available to students. Some may find game markers a real boon in solving the beanbag problem at the top of Sheet 2. Some may find colored tile or 1″ × 1″ paper or cardboard squares in red, blue, and yellow helpful in solving the fraction problem at the top of Sheet 3. Base ten pieces may also help some students complete the addition, subtraction, and multiplication necessary to solve a number of the problems. Limit students' use of calculators this month to the second problem on Sheet 1.

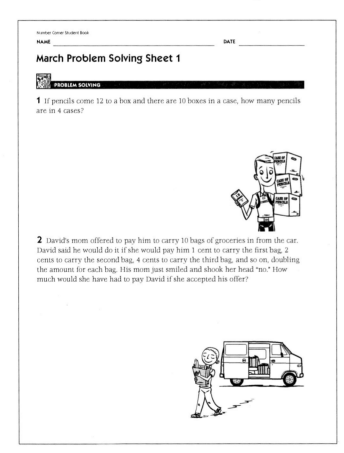

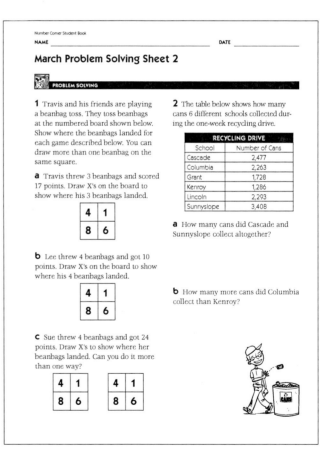

When they have had time to complete one problem, ask students to discuss one or both problems as a class. As you have in past months, encourage them to take the lead in the class discussion. Because most of these problems will pose a significant challenge to many, if not most, students, the discussions are likely to be more interesting and animated than ever. You may find that students need to return to a problem the following week. You might also want

Problem Solving Graphs, Tables & Fractions (cont.)

to invite students to take these problems home or work on them during designated seatwork periods during the day.

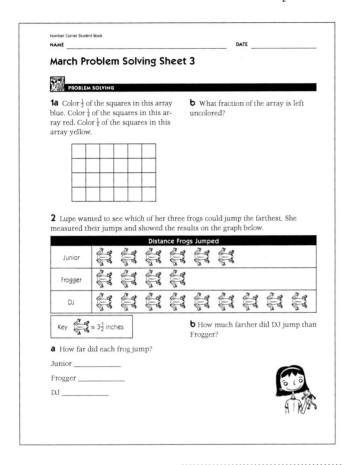

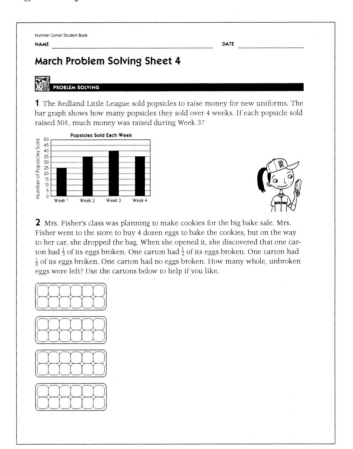

....

Naming the Problem-Solving Strategies *Many of the problems offered this month lend themselves particularly well to one or more of the 7 strategies listed below. Keep in mind that students will also generate their own interesting, and often unexpected, ways to solve each problem.*

- *making a sketch or a picture*
- *using or looking for a pattern*
- *making an organized list*
- *using or making a table or a chart*
- *using logical reasoning*
- *simplifying the problem*
- *guess and check*

You may find it most effective to first invite children to solve the problems any way they can and then ask students to begin classifying the strategies shared during class discussion of the problems. When they do, list the strategies using terms invented by your students, the terms cited above, or the terms commonly used in your school or district.

Problem Solving Graphs, Tables & Fractions (cont.)

The table below is for your reference only. Avoid telling students which strategy to use to solve a particular problem, because we want fourth-graders to use the strategies they find most useful, many of which will be hybrids of two or more strategies. The only time it might be best to suggest a particular strategy is if students seem to be fixated on a single strategy to the exclusion of all others. (Guess and check is a favorite with many fourth graders.) In these cases, you might either gently encourage or firmly insist that a student try something new or solve the problem using two different strategies.

Sheet	Problem	Strategy
1	1	Simplifying the problem
	2	Using or looking for a pattern; making an organized list; using or making a table or chart
2	1	Guess and check
3	1	Making a sketch or picture
	2	Simplifying the problem
4	1	Using logical reasoning; simplifying the problem
	2	Making a sketch or picture

MARCH PROBLEMS AND STRATEGIES

March Number Line

NUMBER LINE

Prime Numbers & Round & Add to the Nearest Tenth

Overview

Students examine the numbers on the Number Line that were not identified as multiples of 2, 3, 4, 5, 6, 7, 8, or 9. In doing so, they revisit the concepts of prime and composite numbers, factors, and multiples. Later in the month, a new version of the familiar game of Round & Add is introduced, in which students round decimal numbers to the nearest tenth.

Frequency

Once a week

Skills & Concepts

★ exploring concepts of prime and composite numbers, factors, and multiples

★ modeling, recognizing, ordering, and rounding decimals to the nearest tenth

★ locating decimals to hundredths on a number line

★ adding decimals to hundredths using money amounts

You'll need

★ Round It to the Nearest Tenth (Overhead NC 7.5)

★ Multiples on the Number Line (Number Corner Student Book, page 71)

★ number line

★ 2 dice, one marked 1–6 and one marked 4–9

★ overhead money value pieces

★ pointer (such as a yard or meter stick)

★ blank overhead transparency or piece of chart paper

★ overhead pens in red and blue

★ piece of paper to mask parts of the transparency

★ crayons

....

Advance Preparation If you have not already done so, mark the multiples of 8 and 9 on the Number Line before the first workout this month.

....

Week 1 Thinking about the Numbers That Never Got Marked

Your students have probably already observed that some numbers on the Number Line never got marked as multiples of 2, 3, 4, 5, 6, 7, 8, or 9. Begin your first workout by asking students to identify those numbers. (It may help to have a student volunteer point to the unmarked numbers with a yardstick or pointer as the rest of the class names them.) List the numbers on a blank transparency or a piece of chart paper as students name them. They should identify the following 22 unmarked numbers:

1, 11, 13, 17, 19, 23, 29, 31, 37, 41, 43, 47, 53, 59, 61, 67, 71, 73, 79, 83, 89, 97

Number Line Prime Numbers & Round & Add to the Nearest Tenth (cont.)

Then ask students to complete page 71 in their Number Corner Student Books in pairs. If someone suggests before beginning the page that all the unmarked numbers are prime, welcome the statement as an interesting conjecture and ask students to consider it as they work. Invite students to talk in pairs and table groups as they work, but make sure everyone knows to fill out his or her own page.

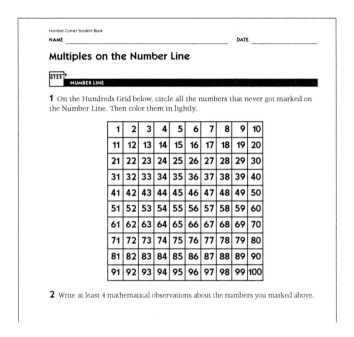

When they are done working, ask students to save these pages for use next week. You'll also need to save the transparency or chart paper on which you listed the numbers.

Week 2 Discussing the Numbers that Never Got Marked

Begin the second workout by asking students to return to page 71 in their Student Books, which they completed last week, and displaying the overhead or chart on which you recorded the unmarked numbers. Ask students to sit in pairs and then have each pair share an observation about the numbers one at a time. This is a wonderful listening exercise, because part of the challenge is to get around the room without repeating a single observation. After each pair has shared one idea, invite students to volunteer any observations that have not yet been shared. It is quite possible that new observations will arise in the context of the discussion. You can also pose questions like those below to elicit additional observations:

• What are the factors of 1, of 11, of 13, of 17, of 29, of 73? (in each case, 1 and the number itself)

• What are the dimensions of rectangular arrays you could draw for 17, 29, 31, 37, 41?

Number Line Prime Numbers & Round & Add to the Nearest Tenth (cont.)

- What is the term mathematicians use to describe numbers that have only themselves and the number 1 for factors? (prime numbers)
- Are all of the numbers on the "not-marked" list prime numbers? (Yes, with the exception of 1, which is neither prime nor composite, since it has just one factor, itself.)
- Does this collection include *all* the prime numbers between 1 and 100? (No. 2, 3, 5, and 7 are also primes, but they have been marked on the line because they were all used as counting numbers in past months.)
- Why do all the numbers on the list have 1, 3, 7, or 9 in the ones place? (It may help for students to discuss the fact that all the numbers that have 2, 4, 5, 6, 8, or 0 in the ones place got marked. These numbers are all either even or multiples of 5.)

Weeks 3 & 4 Round & Add to the Nearest Tenth

In the third and fourth workouts, students play the familiar game of Round & Add, this time to the nearest tenth. If students have studied decimals, this will be familiar territory, but reading, ordering, rounding, and adding decimals are skills that students will need to revisit repeatedly during fourth and fifth grades.

Begin the workout by displaying just the top part of the Round & Add to the Nearest Tenth overhead and working with student input to label the dime and penny with their decimal and fraction names. Next, display the open number line in the middle section of the transparency and invite students to discuss how the marks on the line should be labeled. While some students may suggest labeling them in increments of 10 (10, 20, 30, etc.), you can trust that given their familiarity with money and their previous experiences with the open number line, students will eventually agree that the marks represent tenths (or dimes) and should be labeled 0.10, 0.20, and so on. Once the line has been labeled, ask students where they see the value of a dime. In other words, where on this line do they see one-tenth? What about one-half or 50 cents?

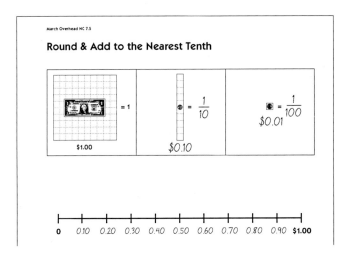

Number Line Prime Numbers & Round & Add to the Nearest Tenth (cont.)

Once the line has been labeled, you'll need 2 dice, 1 marked 1–6 and 1 marked 4–9, and red and blue overhead pens to play the game. You'll take turns with students rolling both dice and arranging the two numbers, placing one in the tenths place and one in the hundredths place. For example, if you roll a 4 and a 7, you can create 0.47 or 0.74. You'll write your number on the line using your color (red or blue) and then circle the number to which it rounds to the nearest tenth (0.50 or 0.70). At the end of the game, you and the students will add up your rounded amounts and your actual amounts. The winner is the player whose rounded and actual totals match most closely. Therefore, when arranging your digits, your goal is to arrange them so that the actual number is as close as possible to the rounded number. For example, if you roll a 4 and a 7, 0.47 is a better choice than 0.74, because it is only 0.03 away from 0.50.

Announce to the class that you're going to play a new version of Round & Add and explain briefly how it is played. Then begin the game by asking a student to roll the dice for you. Record the two numbers on the overhead or the board and discuss your thinking about how to arrange these digits to form a number that is most advantageous to you. As you do, remind students that to round a decimal number to the nearest tenth (or the nearest dime), they need to look at the digit in the hundredths (or pennies) place. If that digit is less than 5, it rounds down; if it is 5 or more, the number rounds up. Use the language of dimes and pennies, and tenths and hundredths, interchangeably to help students move from what they already know well (money) to what they are less familiar with (decimals). For example, if you arrange your digits to form 0.47, you might explain that you'll round it to 0.50 because 47 cents is closer to 50 cents than it is to 40 cents.

Once you have made a decision, record the number where it belongs on the open number line and then circle the tenth to which it rounds. Mark your results in red and the class's results in blue so that you can tell the difference as the game proceeds.

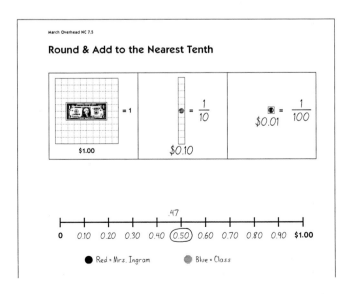

Number Line Prime Numbers & Round & Add to the Nearest Tenth (cont.)

Now have a volunteer roll for the class, discuss how they want to arrange the 2 digits, and then write the number and circle the tenth to which it rounds in blue on the number line. Remind students that they'll need to arrange a number that rounds to something other than the tenth you just claimed. As they discuss their choices and how to round the number, encourage them to talk in terms of cents and to model the amounts with money value pieces if needed.

Continue taking turns until all the tenths have been claimed by one team or the other. If either you or the class roll 2 digits that cannot be rounded to an unclaimed tenth, you lose that turn. You or the students can decide at any time to use just 1 of the dice to try to claim the 0 or 0.10. In that case, the number rolled is assigned to the hundredths place: for example, if a 4 is rolled, it will be considered .04 and rounded to 0.

After all the tenths have been claimed, ask students to find the total of the rounded numbers for you and for them using mental strategies. Then list the actual scores for each team on the board, taking the opportunity to show students how to align the numbers and the decimal points. Have half the class compute your actual total using paper and pencil methods, and have the other half determine the students' actual total. Then have students work together to compare each team's rounded and actual totals; the team whose rounded and actual totals match most closely wins.

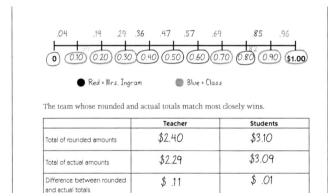

The team whose rounded and actual totals match most closely wins.

	Teacher	Students
Total of rounded amounts	$2.40	$3.10
Total of actual amounts	$2.29	$3.09
Difference between rounded and actual totals	$ .11	$ .01

Teacher's Actual Score	Students' Actual Score
.04	.14
.36	.19
.47	.29
.57	.69
.85	.82
$2.29	.96
	$3.09

Students *Wow! We were only off by 1 cent!*
I think rolling 9's is a good thing in this game because you can use them to get really close to the nearest tenth.
Mrs. Ingram was only off by 11 cents. That's not much. We just got really lucky.
It's funny in this game how it doesn't matter if you get a higher score, just that your two scores are the closest to each other.

March Assessment

ASSESSMENT

Number Corner Checkup 3

Overview

In place of regular workouts, students spend two Number Corner periods completing a four-page skills checkup. The teacher may use a class checklist to record assessment results and get an overview of students' strengths, as well as the areas in which they'll need more work.

Timing

Last week of March or first week of April

Skills & Concepts

★ demonstrating fluency with multiplication and division facts

★ adding and subtracting 2- and 3-digit numbers with regrouping

★ multiplying and dividing a 2-digit number by a 1-digit number

★ solving addition, subtraction, and multiplication story problems

★ selecting an appropriate number to make an equation true

★ finding the area and perimeter of a rectangle

★ reading and interpreting a bar graph and a pictograph

★ predicting the likelihood of an outcome numerically

★ using a variety of physical and visual models to conceptualize fractions

You'll need

★ Number Corner Checkup 3, pages 1–4 (Blacklines NC A 7.1–7.4)

★ Number Corner Checkup 3 Class Checklist, pages 1–3 (Blacklines NC A 7.5–7.7, 2 or 3 copies as needed, optional)

★ base ten pieces and/or colored tile for students who want to use them (Use Blackline NC 1.9 to create your own base ten pieces if needed, and cut 1"-by-1" squares of tag board or construction paper if you do not have colored tile in your classroom.)

Part 1 Number Corner Checkup, Pages 1 & 2

Have students complete the first two pages of the checkup during one of your regular Number Corner periods at the end of March or very early in April. Give them 2 minutes to complete as many of the 40 multiplication facts on

Assessment Number Corner Checkup 3 (cont.)

the first page as they can. If many students are still developing fluency with multiplication facts, stress that this is just a check-in designed to help you and them see which facts they still need to work on. (It may be interesting to compare the number of facts they completed correctly this time to the number they were able to complete correctly at the end of January.) On the other hand, if most of your students are already quite fluent with their multiplication facts, you might consider eliminating this page of the checkup.

After they have had 2 minutes to work on the first page, allow them to complete the second page at their own pace. Make base ten pieces and colored tile available for students to use for any item on the second page.

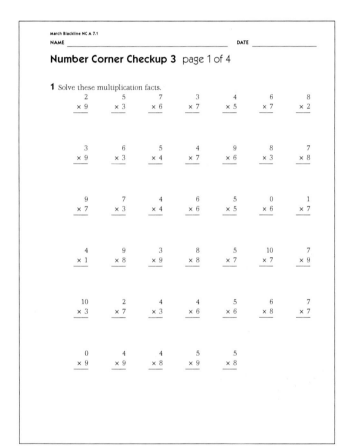

Part 2 Number Corner Checkup, Pages 3 & 4

The day after they have completed the first two pages, give students a full Number Corner period to complete the last two pages of the checkup. Again, make manipulatives available for those who want to use them.

Assessment Number Corner Checkup 3 (cont.)

March Blackline NC A 7.3
NAME _____ DATE _____

Number Corner Checkup 3 page 3 of 4

5 Which equation would be true if 6 were put in the box?

○ 36 ÷ ☐ = 4

○ 18 ÷ ☐ = 3

○ 24 ÷ ☐ = 8

○ 42 ÷ ☐ = 6

6 What number will make this equation true?

$$3 + 5 + \boxed{} = 6 + 9$$

○ 9

○ 15

○ 7

○ 23

7a What is the perimeter of this rectangle?

10 inches

12 inches

b What is the area of this rectangle?

8 Alicia made the graph below to show the number of hours she worked for 4 weeks. If Alicia earned $7.50 an hour, how much money did she earn during Week 1? Show your work.

Hours Worked Each Week

Number of Hours

Week 1 Week 2 Week 3 Week 4

9 There are 3 blue tile and 6 red tile in a paper bag. If Brittany picks a tile from the bag without looking, what is the probability it will be a red tile?

$\frac{6}{12}$ $\frac{3}{6}$ $\frac{6}{9}$ $\frac{6}{6}$

○   ○   ○   ○

March Blackline NC A 7.4
NAME _____ DATE _____

Number Corner Checkup 3 page 4 of 4

10 Shade in $\frac{1}{4}$ on each model below.

a   b   c

d   e

11 In which model is $\frac{2}{3}$ shaded?

○   ○

○   ○

○   ○

12a What fraction of this array is shaded in?

b How do you know?

13 James wants to serve all of this pizza to 12 people. What can he do so that each person can be served an equal amount?

○ Use only half the pizza.

○ Cut each piece in thirds.

○ Cut each piece in half.

○ Cut each piece in sixths.

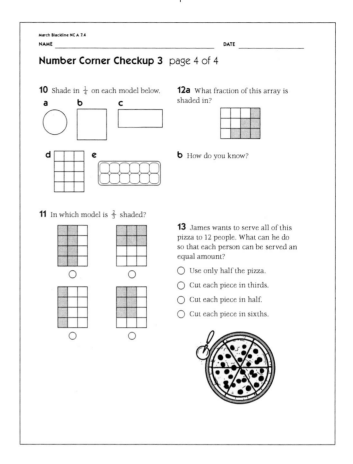

SUPPORT

Students' work on the checkup may indicate that some need continued support with specific skills and concepts. You can have select students use specific Support Activities with a resource room teacher, instructional assistant, and/or parent to improve specific skills and strengthen conceptual understandings. You may find the activities listed below particularly helpful with skills featured on this checkup.

SUPPORT ACTIVITIES		
Activity	**Name**	**Skills**
Activity 12	Spinning Around Multiplication	strategies for multiplication facts up to 6 × 6
Activity 13	Array Challenge	multiplication facts to 8 × 9 with the array model
Activity 14	Multiplication Challenge	multiplication facts to 8 × 8 with a variety of models
Activity 15	Spinning for Arrays	multiplication facts to 8 × 10 with the array model
Activity 16	Product Bingo	practice of multiplication facts to 9 × 9
Activity 17	What's Missing? Bingo	practice of multiplication and division facts to 9 × 6

Assessment Number Corner Checkup 3 (cont.)

SUPPORT ACTIVITIES		
Activity	**Name**	**Skills**
Activity 18	More or Less Addition Big Time	3-digit addition with regrouping
Activity 19	More or Less Subtraction Big Time	3-digit subtraction with regrouping
Activity 20	Larger Numbers on a Line	3-digit subtraction and addition with regrouping
Activity 21	Perimeter Showdown	perimeter and area of rectangles
Activity 22	Spin & Multiply	2-digit by 1-digit multiplication
Activity 23	Remainders Win	division with remainders
Activity 24	Fraction Race	understanding, modeling, and comparing fractions
Activity 25	Fraction Bingo	understanding, modeling, and comparing fractions

March Answer Keys

ANSWER KEY

Assessment Blacklines

Blacklines NC A 7.1–7.4, Number Corner Checkup 3

1 18, 15, 42, 21, 20, 42, 16

27, 18, 20, 28, 54, 24, 56

63, 21, 16, 36, 25, 0, 7

4, 72, 27, 64, 35, 70, 63

30, 14, 12, 24, 30, 48, 49

0, 36, 32, 45, 40

2 3, 5, 4, 4, 9, 12, 8

6, 10, 9, 7, 4, 2, 6

3 a 6441 slices

b 473 more slices

4 a 144

b 120

c 168

d 96

5 $18 \div \square = 3$

6 7

7 a 44 inches

b 120 sq. inches

8 $22.50

9 $^6/_9$

10 a Student responses will vary. Example:

b Student responses will vary. Examples:

example 1:   example 2:   example 3:

c Student responses will vary. Examples:

example 1:   example 2:

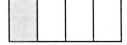

d Student responses will vary. Example:

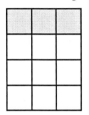

e Student responses will vary. Example:

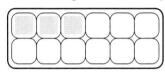

12 a $^1/_2$

b Students' explanations will vary. Examples:

example 1:

Because there's 12 squares and 6 are shaded.

example 2:

Because it looks likes a rectangle cut in half on the diagonal.

13 Cut each piece in half.

Number Corner Student Book

page 70, March Problem Solving Sheet 1

1 480 pencils in 4 cases, Students' work will vary. Example:

12 × 10 = 120 pencils in a case

120 × 4 = 400 + 80 = 480

2 $10.23, Students' work will vary. Example:

bag	price
1	0.01
2	0.02
3	0.04
4	0.08
5	0.16
6	0.32
7	0.64
8	1.28
9	2.56
10	5.12

I used a calculator to add them all up. It was $10.23.

ANSWER KEY

Number Corner Student Book (cont.)

page 71, Multiples on the Number Line

1

(1)	2	3	4	5	6	7	8	9	10
(11)	12	(13)	14	15	16	(17)	18	(19)	20
21	22	(23)	24	25	26	27	28	(29)	30
(31)	32	33	34	35	36	(37)	38	39	40
(41)	42	(43)	44	45	46	(47)	48	49	50
51	52	(53)	54	55	56	57	58	(59)	60
(61)	62	63	64	65	66	(67)	68	69	70
(71)	72	(73)	74	75	76	77	78	(79)	80
81	82	(83)	84	85	86	87	88	(89)	90
91	92	93	94	95	96	(97)	98	99	100

2 Students' observations will vary.

page 73, March Problem Solving Sheet 2

1 a

4	1 ˣ
8 ˣₓ	6

b

4 ˣₓ	1 ˣₓ
8	6

c

4 ˣ	1
8 ˣ	6 ᵧ ₓ

4 ˣₓ	1
8 ˣₓ	6

2 a 5885 cans

b 977 more cans

page 75, March Problem Solving Sheet 3

1 a Students will configure their fractions in a variety of ways. Example:

Y	Y	Y	Y		
R	R	R	R	R	R
B	B	B	B	B	B
B	B	B	B	B	B

b $2/24$ or $1/12$

2 a 21, 14, 31.5

b 17.5 inches farther

page 76, More About Fractions

1 There may be more valid fraction names for some of the fractions below. The ones students are most likely to name are shown below.

Calendar Marker	6	7	8	9	10
1st Fraction Name	$\frac{4}{12}$	$\frac{2}{6}$	$\frac{20}{60}$	$\frac{4}{12}$	$\frac{4}{12}$
2nd Fraction Name	$\frac{1}{3}$ $\frac{2}{6}$	$\frac{1}{3}$	$\frac{4}{12}$ $\frac{1}{3}$ $\frac{2}{6}$	$\frac{1}{3}$ $\frac{2}{6}$	$\frac{1}{3}$ $\frac{2}{6}$

2 Students' responses will vary.

3 It is true that all of the fractions show $1/3$ of something. Students' explanations will vary.

4 $1/2$ is greater than $2/6$. Students' explanations will vary. Example:

$1/2$ is also $3/6$, and $2/6$ is less than $3/6$, so $2/6$ is less than $1/2$.

5

ANSWER KEY

Number Corner Student Book (cont.)

page 77, Looking at Line Graphs

1 Graph C

2 Graph D

3 Graph B

4 Graph A

page 78, March Problem Solving Sheet 4

1 $20 was raised in week 3, Students' work will vary.
Example:
50¢ is half a dollar, so if they sold 40 popsicles, they
would have half that many dollars. So it's $20.

2 36 whole unbroken eggs were left. Students' methods
will vary. Examples:
example 1:

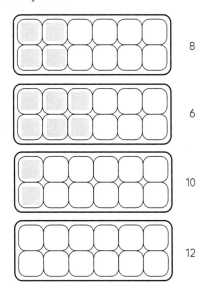

8 + 6 + 10 + 12 = 16 + 20 = 36

example 2:
There were 48 eggs, and then I subtracted the ones that
broke. So it's 48 – 4 – 6 – 2 = 48 – 12 = 36

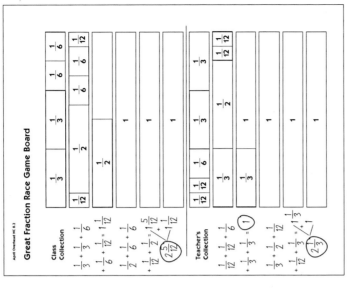

April Overhead NC 8.2

Great Fraction Race Game Board

Class Collection

| $\frac{1}{3}$ | | $\frac{1}{3}$ | | $\frac{1}{3}$ | | $\frac{1}{6}$ |
| | | | | | | |

$\frac{1}{12}$ $\frac{1}{2}$ ... $\frac{1}{6}$ $\frac{1}{6}$

$\frac{1}{3} + \frac{1}{3} + \frac{1}{6} =$

$+ \frac{1}{6} + \frac{1}{12} = 1\frac{1}{12}$

$\frac{1}{2} + \frac{1}{6} + \frac{1}{6} =$

$+ \frac{1}{6} + \frac{1}{2} = \frac{5}{12}$

⊘ $2\frac{5}{12}$ ... $\frac{1}{12}$

Teacher's Collection

$\frac{1}{12} + \frac{1}{12} =$

$\frac{1}{3} + \frac{1}{3} =$ ①

$\frac{1}{12} + \frac{1}{2} + \frac{1}{12} =$

$+ \frac{1}{3} + \frac{1}{3} = 1\frac{1}{3}$

⊘ $2\frac{1}{3}$ ... $\frac{1}{1}$

Calendar Collector

April Calendar Record Sheet

Date	Shape Name	Calculations	Perimeter Total
1	Equilateral Triangle	$1 + 1 + 1 = 3$ or $3 \times 1 =$	3 cm
2	Rectangle	$(2 \times 1) + (2 \times 2) =$	6 cm
3	Regular Pentagon	$1 + 1 + 1 + 1 =$	5 cm
4	Isosceles Triangle	$3 + 3 + 2 =$	8 cm
5	Trapezoid	$3 + 1 + 1 + 2 =$	7 cm
6	Regular Pentagon	$2 + 2 + 2 + 2 + 2 = 10$ or $5 \times 2 =$	10 cm
7	Equilateral Triangle	$3 + 3 + 3 = 9$ or $3 \times 3 =$	9 cm
8	Square	$3 + 3 + 3 + 3 = 12$ or $4 \times 3 =$	12 cm
9	Pentagon	$1 + 2 + 2 + 3 + 3 =$	11 cm
10	Isosceles Triangle	$5 + 5 + 4$ or $(2 \times 5) + 4 =$	14 cm
11	Trapezoid	$3 + 3 + 3 + 4$ or $(3 \times 3) + 4 =$	13 cm
12	Pentagon	$2 + (2 \times 3) + (2 \times 4) =$	16 cm
13	Equilateral Triangle	$5 \times 3 =$	15 cm
14	Rectangle	$2 + 2 + 7 + 7$ or $(2 \times 2) + (2 \times 7) =$	18 cm
15	Pentagon	$6 + 2 + 3 + 2 + 4 =$	17 cm
16	Scalene Triangle	$4 + 7 + 9 =$	20 cm
17	Trapezoid	$8 + 3 + 5 + 3 =$	19 cm
18	Pentagon	$(2 \times 6) + (2 \times 3) + 4 =$	22 cm

April

Sunday	Monday	Tuesday	Wednesday	Thursday	Friday	Saturday

Calendar Grid

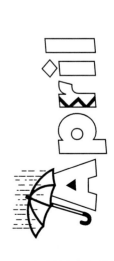

Division Capture Instructions

+|× **COMPUTATIONAL FLUENCY**

1 Each player rolls the 1–6 die once. The player with the higher number gets to choose what color he or she wants to be and gets to take the first turn. Then write your names and fill in the color boxes at the top of your record sheet.

2 Roll the die and use the number you get to make one of the equations in the grid true. There will be more than one number that will work for any number. Write the number in the box using your color.

3 Take turns until all the boxes are filled. (If you roll a number you can't use, you lose that turn.) Both players fill in every turn on their own record sheets. Try to capture 3 or 4 boxes in a row—across, up and down, or diagonally. After all the boxes are filled, help each other use a calculator to check the answers. Then circle the places on the grid where you got 3 or 4 equations in a row and figure your scores.

4 Now play another round of the game!

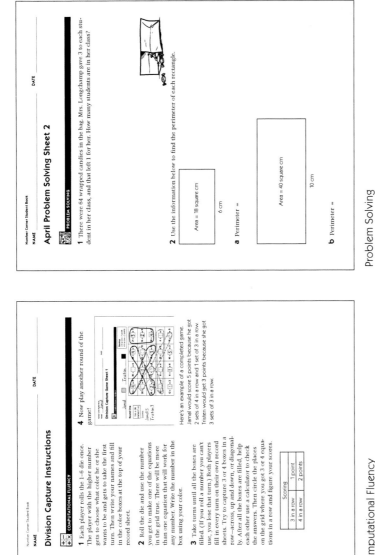

Here's an example of a completed game. Jamal would score 5 points because he got 2 sets of 4 in a row and 1 set of 3 in a row. Tristen would get 3 points because she got 3 sets of 3 in a row.

Scoring	
3 in a row	1 point
4 in a row	2 points

Computational Fluency

April Problem Solving Sheet 2

PROBLEM SOLVING

1 There were 64 wrapped candies in the bag. Mrs. Longchamp gave 3 to each student in her class, and that left 1 for her. How many students are in her class?

2 Use the information below to find the perimeter of each rectangle.

Area = 18 square cm

6 cm

a Perimeter =

Area = 40 square cm

10 cm

b Perimeter =

Problem Solving

Decimal Draw Game Sheet 1

NUMBER LINE

Game 1

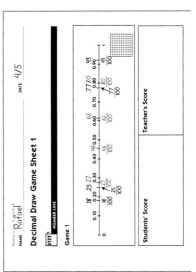

Students' Score

Teacher's Score

Number Line

What's Going to Happen in April?

The workouts this month feature key skills and concepts for the fourth grade year: fraction and decimal sense, early computation with fractions and decimals, the difference between area and perimeter, division facts, and multiplicative thinking. Through an engaging calendar pattern, three games, and a variety of problem-solving opportunities, students are provided with the repeated exposure and practice they need to develop facility with these skills and concepts.

Calendar Grid

The April Calendar Grid pattern features a repeating sequence of triangles, quadrilaterals, and pentagons whose perimeters grow over the course of the month. The class will keep a record of the kinds of shapes featured on the markers, as well as the perimeters of those shapes.

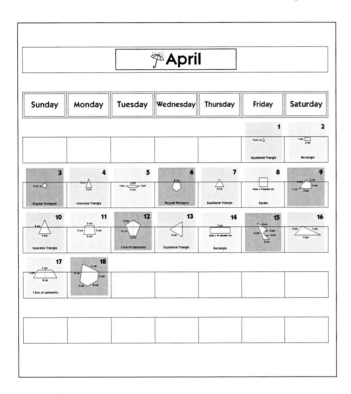

April Calendar Record Sheet			
Date	Shape Name	Perimeter	
		Calculations	Total
1	Equilateral Triangle	1 + 1 + 1 = 3 or 3 × 1 =	3 cm
2	Rectangle	(2 × 1) + (2 × 2) =	6 cm
3	Regular Pentagon	1 + 1 + 1 + 1 + 1 =	5 cm
4	Isosceles Triangle	3 + 3 + 2 =	8 cm
5	Trapezoid	3 + 1 + 1 + 2 =	7 cm
6	Regular Pentagon	2 + 2 + 2 + 2 + 2 = 10 or 5 × 2 =	10 cm
7	Equilateral Triangle	3 + 3 + 3 = 9 or 3 × 3 =	9 cm
8	Square	3 + 3 + 3 + 3 = 12 or 4 × 3 =	12 cm
9	Pentagon	1 + 2 + 2 + 3 + 3 =	11 cm
10	Isosceles Triangle	5 + 5 + 4 or (2 × 5) + 4 =	14 cm
11	Trapezoid	3 + 3 + 3 + 4 or (3 × 3) + 4 =	13 cm
12	Pentagon	2 + (2 × 3) + (2 × 4) =	16 cm
13	Equilateral Triangle	5 × 3 =	15 cm
14	Rectangle	2 + 2 + 7 + 7 or (2 × 2) + (2 × 7) =	18 cm
15	Pentagon	6 + 2 + 3 + 2 + 4 =	17 cm
16	Scalene Triangle	4 + 7 + 9 =	20 cm
17	Trapezoid	8 + 3 + 5 + 3 =	19 cm
18	Pentagon	(2 × 6) + (2 × 3) + 4 =	22 cm

Students must use the information provided to determine the perimeter of the shape on that marker. For example, the 12th marker (shown below) features an irregular pentagon with 1 line of symmetry and measurements for just 3 of the 5 sides. Students must apply their understanding of line symmetry to determine that the two unmarked sides are 3 cm and 4 cm in length. To conclude that the perimeter is 16 cm, students must understand that the perimeter of any closed figure is the total distance around it.

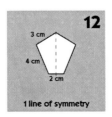

The pattern this month is intended to help students develop a better understanding of area and perimeter, increased skill at computing the perimeters of shapes other than squares and rectangles, and greater confidence at making deductions about 2-dimensional shapes.

Calendar Collector

In this month's Calendar Collector Workout, the teacher and students collect fraction strips cut into twelfths, sixths, thirds, and halves, racing each other over the course of the month to amass a total of 6 whole strips. This workout builds on the Equivalent Fractions calendar pattern from March and provides multiple opportunities to explore equivalent fractions, mixed numbers, and addition of fractions with like and unlike denominators.

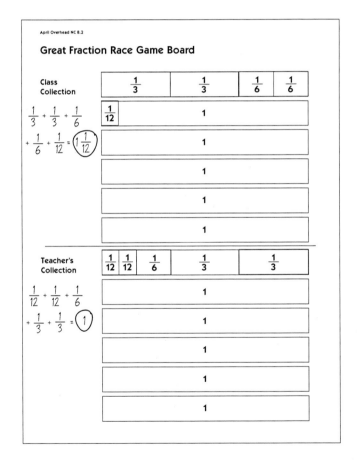

Computational Fluency

The Computational Fluency Workout provides practice with basic division facts in the context of a simple but engaging game called Division Capture. To play the game, players take turns rolling a 1–6 die and using the number that comes up to complete one of 20 division equations on a grid. The results of each roll are recorded on a single sheet, with each partner using a different color. Once all 20 equations have been completed, players loop any equations they have captured in horizontal, vertical, or diagonal rows. One point is awarded for 3 boxes in a row, and 2 points are awarded for 4 boxes in a row. The player with the most points wins. Students will play as a class against the teacher as an introduction to the game, and for the rest of the month, they will play in pairs.

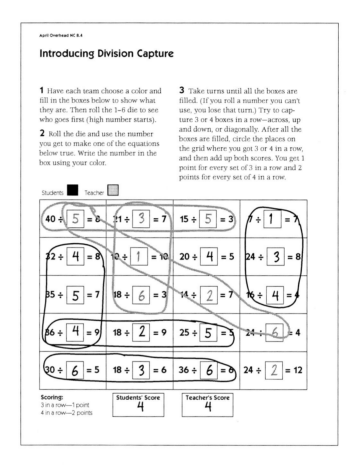

Division Capture offers practice with the basic division facts for all students, and a challenge version of the game is provided for students who have greater fluency with those facts. Playing the game also requires careful strategizing, as there is more than one equation that can be satisfied by any number rolled on the die. Players must consider all of their choices and select their equation carefully to get 3 or 4 equations in a row and try to prevent their opponent from doing the same.

Problem Solving

The Problem Solving Workouts continue to offer multi-step problems. Two of the problems involve adding fractions with like denominators, and one challenges students to find the perimeter of 2 different rectangles based on information about one side and the total area. Many of the problems involve 2- or 3-digit by 1-digit multiplication or division, offering students the chance to develop increasingly efficient and insightful ways to solve such computations.

Number Line

This month's Number Line Workout features a whole-class game in which players order decimals along a 0–1 number line and then add them. The player with the highest total wins.

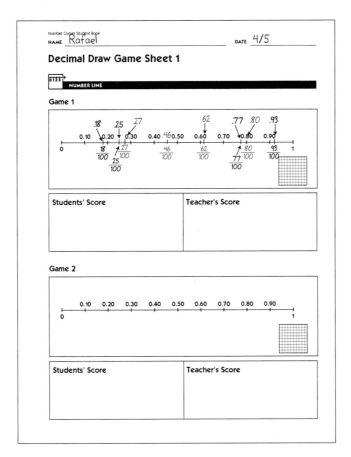

Although students will have already worked in depth with decimals, this game provides repeated practice with ordering fractions and decimals, identifying equivalent fractions and decimals, and adding decimal numbers to the hundredths place. Students need repeated exposure in a variety of contexts to master these skills and concepts with decimal numbers and fractions.

Planning for April

You can use the planning guide below as shown or adapt it to fit the needs of your students and your school schedule.

APRIL PLANNING GUIDE						
Key ★ = Discuss ☆ = Update SB = Number Corner Student Book	MON	TUES	WED	THURS	FRI	SB
Calendar Grid, pp. 307–312 Perimeter Puzzles • using properties of shapes to determine the lengths of their sides and perimeters • identifying, describing, comparing, and classifying shapes • understanding the difference between perimeter and area	★	☆	☆	☆	★	pp. 84 & 91
Calendar Collector, pp. 313–318 The Great Fraction Race • modeling, comparing, reading, and writing fractions and mixed numbers • using physical and visual models to conceptualize fractions and mixed numbers • exploring equivalent fractions and using equivalence to compare fractions • adding fractions and mixed numbers using concrete models	☆	★	☆	☆	☆	pp. 80 & 81
Computational Fluency, pp. 319–322 Division Capture • developing efficient strategies for solving basic division facts			★			pp. 85, 86, 88 & 92
Problem Solving, pp. 323–326 Multiplication & Division Story Problems, Area, Perimeter & Fractions • adding and subtracting 2- and 3-digit numbers with and without regrouping • multiplying and dividing 2- and 3-digit numbers by 1-digit numbers • adding commonly used fractions • developing strategies for finding the perimeter and area of rectangles				★		pp. 82, 87, 89 & 93
Number Line, pp. 327–332 Decimal Draw • modeling, recognizing, and ordering decimals • recognizing equivalent forms of common fractions and decimals • locating decimals to hundredths on a number line • adding decimals					★	pp. 83, 90

Materials You'll Need for April

Manipulatives
- Calendar Grid pocket chart
- about 30 base ten units for each pair of students (Use Blackline NC 1.9 if needed.)
- about 26 red linear units for each pair of students if you have them
- 2 dice, one marked 1–6 and the other 4–9, for each pair of students
- half-class set of calculators
- overhead spinner overlay

Number Corner Calendar Markers
- Day, Month, and Year markers
- Perimeter Puzzle calendar markers

General Materials
- half-class set of rulers with centimeters
- overhead pens in red and black
- a few blank transparencies
- colored pencils including red
- scissors
- glue sticks
- class set of resealable plastic sandwich bags
- piece of paper to mask parts of the overhead

Calendar Grid
Run 1 copy each of Blacklines NC 8.1 and 8.2. Trim them and then glue them together to form one long chart. Post the chart on your calendar display before conducting the first Calendar Grid Workout this month.

Calendar Collector
Before you conduct the first Calendar Collector Workout this month, run and cut copies of Blacklines NC 8.3–8.6 as directed at the top of the sheets. You'll need light blue, light yellow, light green, and light pink copy paper to do this.

Number Line
Before the first Number Line Workout this month, cut apart the overhead Decimal Draw Cards and then store them in a small, sturdy manila envelope or in a resealable plastic bag for repeated use this month and in future years.

Number Corner Overheads
NC 8.1	Great Fraction Race Spinner & Record Sheet
NC 8.2	Great Fraction Race Game Board
NC 8.3	Fraction Strips (cut apart into strips)
NC 8.4	Introducing Division Capture
NC 8.5	April Problem Solving Sheet 1
NC 8.6	Decimal Draw
NC 8.7 & 8.8	Decimal Draw Cards, pages 1 and 2
NC 8.9	April Problem Solving Sheet 2
NC 8.10	April Problem Solving Sheet 3
NC 8.11	April Problem Solving Sheet 4

Number Corner Blacklines
NC 1.1	Monthly Planner Template (1 copy, optional)
NC 1.9	Base Ten Pieces (run as needed)
NC 6.5	Problem Solving Solution Page (4 class sets, optional)
NC 8.1 & 8.2	April Calendar Grid Record Sheet, pages 1 and 2
NC 8.3	Fraction Strips: Halves
NC 8.4	Fraction Strips: Thirds
NC 8.5	Fraction Strips: Sixths
NC 8.6	Fraction Strips: Twelfths
NC 8.7	Base Ten Grid Paper (run as needed)
NC 8.8	Centimeter Grid Paper (class set)
NC 8.9 & 8.10	April Problem Strips, pages 1 and 2 (class set cut into strips along dotted lines, optional)

Number Corner Student Book
pages 80 & 81	Great Fraction Race Record Sheet, pages 1 and 2
page 82	April Problem Solving Sheet 1
page 83	Decimal Draw Game Sheet 1
page 84	A Closer Look at the Perimeter Pattern
page 85	Division Capture Instructions
page 86	Division Capture Game Sheet 1
page 87	April Problem Solving Sheet 2
page 88	Division Capture Game Sheet 2
page 89	April Problem Solving Sheet 3
page 90	Decimal Draw Game Sheet 2
page 91	More Perimeters & a Triangle Problem
page 92	Division Capture Game Sheet 3
page 93	April Problem Solving Sheet 4

April Calendar Grid

 CALENDAR GRID

Perimeter Puzzles

STUDENT BOOK

Overview

This month's calendar pattern features a repeating sequence of triangles, quadrilaterals, and pentagons whose perimeters grow over the course of the month. Students must use the information on each marker to determine the perimeter of the shape, which gives them a chance to apply their knowledge of geometry, as well as their deductive reasoning skills. Students also practice computing the perimeters of shapes other than squares and rectangles and develop a deeper understanding of the difference between area and perimeter.

Frequency

Update the Calendar Grid and record sheet each day, and share observations and predictions at least once a week.

Skills & Concepts

★ using properties of shapes to determine the lengths of their sides and perimeters

★ identifying, describing, comparing, and classifying shapes

★ identifying line symmetry in 2-D shapes

★ identifying shapes with parallel sides

★ describing, extending, and making generalizations about patterns

★ extending number sequences that increase and decrease in a predictable manner

★ making the distinction between perimeter and area (linear units and square units)

You'll need

★ April Calendar Grid Record Sheet, pages 1 and 2 (Blacklines NC 8.1 and 8.2, see Advance Preparation)

★ A Closer Look at the Perimeter Pattern (Number Corner Student Book, page 84)

★ More Perimeters & a Triangle Problem (Number Corner Student Book, page 91)

★ Calendar Grid pocket chart

★ Day, Month, and Year markers

★ Perimeter Puzzle calendar markers

★ about 30 base ten units for each pair of students or Centimeter Grid Paper (Blackline NC 8.8, class set)

★ about 26 red linear units for each pair of students if you have them

★ half-class set of rulers with centimeters

Advance Preparation Run 1 copy each of Blacklines NC 8.1 and 8.2. Trim them and then glue them together to form one long chart. Post the chart on your calendar display before conducting the first Calendar Grid Workout this month.

Calendar Grid Perimeter Puzzles (cont.)

···

Week 1 Introducing & Discussing the First Few Calendar Markers (Day 3 or 4)

Open the first Calendar Grid Workout by posting the markers for each day that has passed this month, including today.

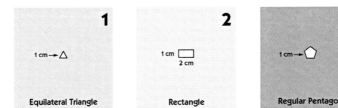

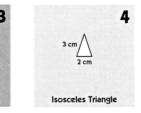

Ask students to observe the markers quietly for a few moments and then discuss their observations with a partner. After a few minutes of discussion, reconvene the class and have a few volunteers share what they noticed. Then work with student input to enter information about the markers on this month's record sheet. As you do, emphasize the importance of labeling each perimeter with the proper units (centimeters). To calculate the perimeters, students will need to draw upon what they know about the properties of each shape, and you may need to review some of the vocabulary with them (e.g., an equilateral triangle has 3 equal sides, while an isosceles triangle only has 2 equal sides; a regular polygon has all equal sides and angles).

> **Teacher** *On our record sheet, we need to fill in the perimeter for each shape. What is the perimeter of this first shape, the equilateral triangle?*
>
> **Sam** *We can't tell. It only tells you that one side is 1 centimeter.*
>
> **Madelyn** *But if it's an equilateral triangle, all the sides are the same. So they're all 1.*
>
> **Brittany** *Can you really find the perimeter of a triangle? We only did that for arrays so far.*
>
> **Teacher** *The perimeter is the distance around a shape. So what do you all think? Can we find the perimeter of a triangle, or a pentagon for that matter too?*
>
> **Jorge** *Since it's on the record sheet, I bet we can!*
>
> **Antoine** *Right, so it would just be 3. Because each side is 1, so it's 3 times 1. 3 centimeters.*

Calendar Grid Perimeter Puzzles (cont.)

Date	Shape Name	Perimeter	
		Calculations	Total
1	Equilateral Triangle	1 + 1 + 1 = 3 or 3 × 1 =	3 cm
2	Rectangle	(2 × 1) + (2 × 2) =	6 cm
3	Regular Pentagon	1 + 1 + 1 + 1 + 1 =	5 cm
4	Isosceles Triangle	3 + 3 + 2 =	8 cm

April Calendar Record Sheet

When you have filled in the information, ask students to share observations about these perimeters. It's too early for them to detect a pattern from one perimeter to the next, but drawing their attention to these numbers right now ensures that they keep an eye on them throughout the month. (As the days pass, students will notice that the perimeter increases by 3 centimeters, decreases by 1 centimeter, and then repeats this pattern.)

Week 2 Completing a Student Book Page (Day 10 or 11)

Open the second workout by having students work in pairs to complete page 84 in the Number Corner Student Book, which asks them to compute the perimeters of the first 10 shapes and record as many observations about them as they can. Encourage students to work together, but to fill out their own sheets. Many observations can be made about this set of markers, and you can help students focus a bit by encouraging them to look for patterns among the shapes and their perimeters and by reminding them to consider such attributes as parallel sides and symmetry, as well as the number of sides and types of angles within the shapes.

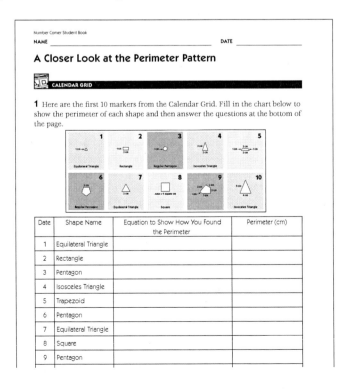

Calendar Grid Perimeter Puzzles (cont.)

It will take most, if not all, of one Number Corner period for students to complete this page. Try to make time the next day for each student pair to share one observation they made about the pattern. Challenge the class to make it all the way around the room without repeating an observation, and then invite students to share more observations if they have some that have not been shared after each pair has made a contribution.

Week 3 Making Predictions & Discussing Markers 8 & 14 (around day 18)

Open your third workout by having students talk first in pairs and then as a whole group about how they can use the information on the grid and record sheet to give a complete description of the marker that will be posted today.

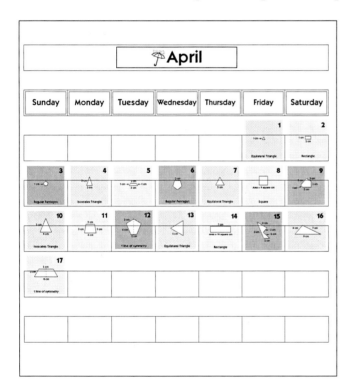

	April Calendar Record Sheet		
Date	Shape Name	Perimeter	
		Calculations	Total
1	Equilateral Triangle	$1 + 1 + 1 = 3$ or $3 \times 1 =$	3 cm
2	Rectangle	$(2 \times 1) + (2 \times 2) =$	6 cm
3	Regular Pentagon	$1 + 1 + 1 + 1 + 1 =$	5 cm
4	Isosceles Triangle	$3 + 3 + 2 =$	8 cm
5	Trapezoid	$3 + 1 + 1 + 2 =$	7 cm
6	Regular Pentagon	$2 + 2 + 2 + 2 + 2 = 10$ or $5 \times 2 =$	10 cm
7	Equilateral Triangle	$3 + 3 + 3 = 9$ or $3 \times 3 =$	9 cm
8	Square	$3 + 3 + 3 + 3 = 12$ or $4 \times 3 =$	12 cm
9	Pentagon	$1 + 2 + 2 + 3 + 3 =$	11 cm
10	Isosceles Triangle	$5 + 5 + 4$ or $(2 \times 5) + 4 =$	14 cm
11	Trapezoid	$3 + 3 + 3 + 4$ or $(3 \times 3) + 4 =$	13 cm
12	Pentagon	$2 + (2 \times 3) + (2 \times 4) =$	16 cm
13	Equilateral Triangle	$5 \times 3 =$	15 cm
14	Rectangle	$2 + 2 + 7 + 7$ or $(2 \times 2) + (2 \times 7) =$	18 cm
15	Pentagon	$6 + 2 + 3 + 2 + 4 =$	17 cm
16	Scalene Triangle	$4 + 7 + 9 =$	20 cm
17	Trapezoid	$8 + 3 + 5 + 3 =$	19 cm

Students *We said today's marker has to be a pentagon because that's the pattern. Triangle, quadrilateral, pentagon. The one on Sunday was a quadrilateral, so today's has to be a pentagon.*

Also, if you look down the diagonal, you can see it's going to be a pentagon. We think it's going to have a perimeter of 22 because it's going to go up by 3 centimeters today, and 19 + 3 = 22. It keeps going up 3 and going down 1. Today's a going up day.

It won't have all 5 sides the same length because 22 isn't a multiple of 5.

Calendar Grid Perimeter Puzzles (cont.)

> *If it was going to be 20 or 25, all the sides could be equal, but not with 22 centimeters.*
>
> *We think it might be symmetrical, though. If you look down the diagonal, the pentagons on the 6th and the 12th are both symmetrical, so maybe today's will be too.*

After students have had a chance to share and explain their predictions, post the marker for the day and update the record sheet. Then pull out markers 8 and 14 and post them along your whiteboard tray. Ask students how the information on the cards allows them to calculate the perimeter without measuring each side. Invite students to use the grid paper (or base ten units if you have them) to draw or build arrays to explain how they can determine the perimeter based upon information about the area of a rectangle or square.

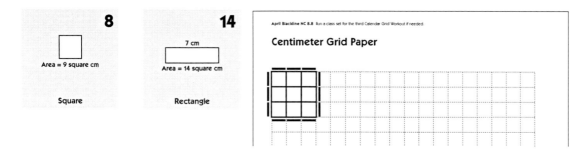

> **Students** *This is the only square you can make with 9 square centimeters. You can make a 1 × 9 rectangle too, but only this one square.*
>
> *The sides on it are 3 centimeters. They have to be because each little square is 1 centimeter on each side.*
>
> *So the perimeter is 3 + 3 + 3 + 3. It's 12.*
>
> *I thought it looked like about 3 centimeters on each side.*
>
> *But we don't even have to measure with a ruler to be sure.*

If they form a rectangle with 14 square centimeters that is 7 centimeters along one side, some students may recognize that this is the rectangular array model for division, in which 14 is the total area of a rectangle and the divisor, 7, is one dimension of that rectangle. They will be able to see that the quotient, the other dimension, is 2. Therefore, the perimeter is 18 (2 + 7 + 2 + 7 = 18).

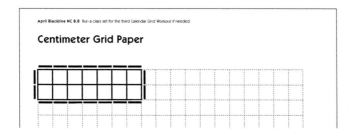

Although some students may not fully grasp these ideas today, the discussion will be mathematically rich and will provide fourth graders with yet another

Calendar Grid Perimeter Puzzles (cont.)

opportunity to make the distinction between perimeter and area and between linear and square units.

....

Week 4 Completing a Student Book Page (on or after day 21)

In the last workout of the month, ask students to complete Student Book page 91, which asks them to calculate the perimeters of markers 17 through 21 and draw at least 3 different isosceles triangles with a perimeter of 26 centimeters. While some may reason or guess and check their way to some solutions for this last problem, others may benefit from having access to 26 linear units (if you have them) to move around or a centimeter ruler so they can draw the triangles to scale. You may also have some or all of your students work in pairs or small groups to solve this problem, which may pose a significant challenge for some students.

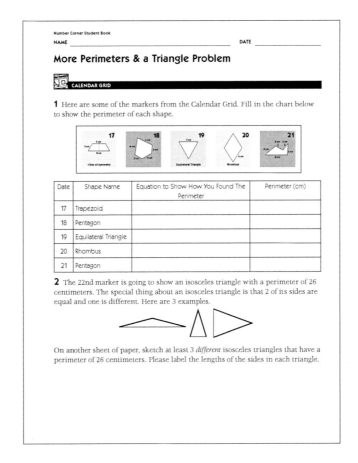

April Calendar Collector

 CALENDAR COLLECTOR

The Great Fraction Race

STUDENT BOOK

Overview

This Calendar Collector Workout builds on the Equivalent Fractions calendar pattern from March. The students and teacher collect paper strips cut into twelfths, sixths, thirds, and halves each day, racing over the course of several weeks to amass a collection that amounts to 6 whole strips. This workout provides multiple opportunities to explore equivalent fractions, mixed numbers, and addition of fractions with like and unlike denominators.

Frequency

Update the collections daily, and share observations and predictions as a whole group once or twice a week.

Skills & Concepts

★ modeling, comparing, reading, and writing fractions and mixed numbers

★ using physical and visual models to conceptualize fractions and mixed numbers

★ exploring equivalent fractions and using equivalence to compare fractions

★ adding fractions and mixed numbers using concrete models

You'll need

★ Great Fraction Race Spinner & Record Sheet (Overhead NC 8.1)

★ Great Fraction Race Game Board (Overhead NC 8.2)

★ Fraction Strips (Overhead NC 8.3; cut apart into strips)

★ Fraction Strips: Halves, Thirds, Sixths, and Twelfths (Blacklines NC 8.3–8.6, see Advance Preparation)

★ Great Fraction Race Record Sheet, pages 1 and 2 (Number Corner Student Book, pages 80 and 81)

★ overhead spinner overlay

★ ruler

★ overhead pen

★ scissors

★ glue sticks

★ class set of resealable plastic sandwhich bags

Advance Preparation Before you conduct the first Calendar Collector Workout this month, run and cut copies of Blacklines NC 8.3–8.6 as directed at the top of the sheets. You'll need light blue, light yellow, light green, and light pink copy paper to do this.

Week 1 Introducing the Great Fraction Race

Introduce this month's Calendar Collector activity by displaying 2 half strips, 3 third strips, 6 sixth strips, and 12 twelfth strips as shown on the next page. Use a ruler to line them up neatly. Ask students to share, first in pairs and then as a class, observations about these strips.

Calendar Collector The Great Fraction Race (cont.)

$\frac{1}{2}$		$\frac{1}{2}$	

(fraction strip diagram showing halves, thirds, sixths, and twelfths)

Students *Each fraction is a different color.*
There are 2 halves in a whole.
There are 3 thirds in a whole.
Hey, the number matches the fraction! There are 6 sixths and 12 twelfths in a whole.
I can see that two-sixths fit into a third.
The thirds and the halves don't match, though. They'll never fit together.
Two twelfths fit into a sixth and three-sixths fit into a half though.

After students have had a chance to share their observations, display the Fraction Race Game Board overhead. Explain that this month, you and the class will each collect a fraction every day, and you'll be racing to fill 6 whole strips. Finally, show the spinner and record sheet.

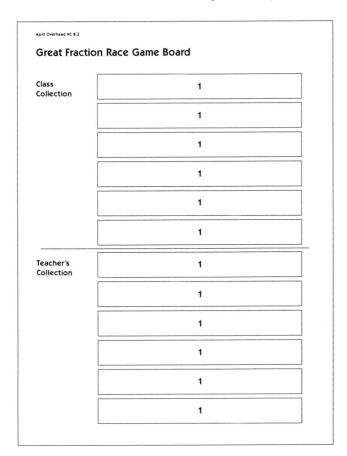

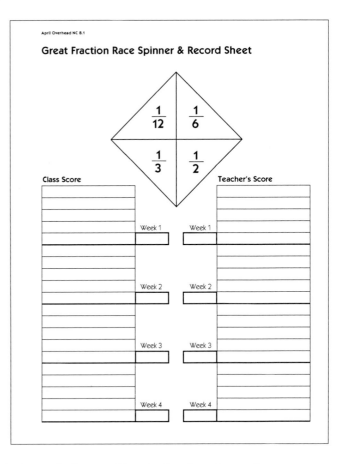

Let students know that each day, a helper will spin the fraction spinner twice—once for the class and once for the teacher—and record the results on the charts below the spinner. Then, when they meet as a class once a week,

Calendar Collector The Great Fraction Race (cont.)

they will work together to add to their collection and yours. You'll use the transparent fraction strips at the overhead to show both collections, and they will glue matching paper fraction strips to two pages in their Student Books to track the progress of each team.

Distribute copies of the paper fraction strips while students get out their scissors. After all the copies have been distributed, each student should have 12 halves, 12 thirds, 12 sixths, and 12 twelfths. Ask students to cut out their pieces carefully and organize them into stacks on their desks or tables. The sixths and twelfths are tiny and will need to be cut carefully, but they don't have to be perfect. Encourage students who finish this task quickly and easily to help neighbors so that within a few minutes, everyone has the same collection of colored fraction strips. As they cut their pieces, organize your transparent pieces into stacks at the overhead.

Finally, ask a volunteer to come up to the overhead, spin the spinner for the class and for you, and record the two fractions in the appropriate spots on the record sheet.

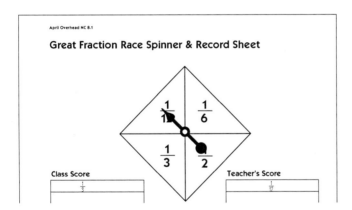

Have students locate the two fractions that were just spun and set them apart from the rest of their collection. How do the two compare? Who is ahead and by how much? Can they use any of the other pieces in their collection to help make comparisons?

Alec We got ¹/3 and you only got ¹/12. We're ahead already!

Calendar Collector The Great Fraction Race (cont.)

Jorge We're ahead of you by ³/₁₂. Can I show at the overhead? See, you have ¹/₁₂, and it takes 3 more twelfths put with that one to make ¹/₃.

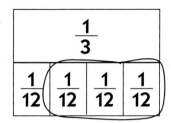

Tristen I think we're ahead of Mrs. Nash by ¹/₄.

Jorge But there aren't any fourths in here!

Tristen Look at this. See? Three-twelfths is half of the ¹/₂ strip, and half of a half is a fourth.

Conclude the first workout by having each student put all the fraction strips into a resealable plastic bag. Collect the bags and save them for the following week, or have students store them in a safe place.

....

Week 2 Building & Recording the Collections of Fractions

Open the second workout by displaying the Great Fraction Race Spinner & Record Sheet overhead. There should be 5 fractions listed for each team. (If this is not the case, have a helper make and record any missing spins before the workout so you have 5 days' worth of fractions to examine with the class.)

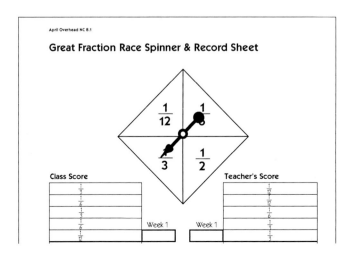

Calendar Collector The Great Fraction Race (cont.)

Ask students to look at the fractions recorded for you and for them. Ask them to talk in pairs and then as a class about what they notice and about who they think will win once they have built both collections.

> **Students** *Mrs. Nash got 2 twelfths in a row. That's pretty bad luck.*
> *We both got $^1/_3$ twice so far.*
> *We got 2 sixths, and that's the same as another third.*
> *When we add them all up, I think we're going to be ahead, but not by much.*

Now have students take out their fraction strips, a pencil, and a glue stick, and then turn to pages 80 and 81 in their Student Books. Ask them to record the fractions the class collected at the bottom of page 80 and then set those fraction pieces on the strips to find their total. Encourage them to arrange the pieces in any order that makes sense to them and to make trades if they need to in order to fill one strip at a time. As they work, encourage them to look at their neighbors' collections. They may find that they are arranging the pieces differently, which is to be expected, and conversations about equivalent fractions will ensue. Have them glue the strips down once they have arranged their pieces to their own satisfaction. The biggest challenge the class may face is how to name and record the total, which is likely to be a mixed number (a whole and a fractional part), and you may need to model the standard notation for a mixed number at the overhead.

Once they have determined and recorded their total, have students repeat the process for your collection, using page 81. When they have determined and recorded your current total, display both collections on the overhead and take a few minutes to have them compare the two collections. Ask them to determine who is ahead and by how much, and then figure out how much more each team will have to collect to complete another whole strip. Then ask them how much more each team needs to reach the goal of 6 whole strips.

Calendar Collector The Great Fraction Race (cont.)

Students *We're ahead by one-twelfth.*
I didn't know Mrs. Nash's strips would fit together exactly to make 1.
Those 2 twelfths she got make one-sixth. One-sixth plus one-sixth is a third, and three-thirds is a whole.
We need eleven-twelfths to fill our next strip, but at least we have a start on it.
We need to fill up 4 and eleven-twelfths to win, but Mrs. Nash still needs 5 to win.
I hope we spin a bunch of halves this week. Then we'd really be ahead!

Weeks 3 & 4 Building & Recording the Collections of Fractions

Have a student helper spin and record a fraction for you and for the class each day. Each time you conduct the Calendar Collector Workout as a class, have students record the fractions collected for both teams and then add to the collections in their Student Books, generating the teams' cumulative totals each week. Ideally, one team or the other will reach or exceed a total of 6 whole strips by the end of the month. If not, the team with the larger total at the end of the last Calendar Collector Workout this month wins the Great Fraction Race.

April Computational Fluency

COMPUTATIONAL FLUENCY

Division Capture

Overview

This month's Computational Fluency Workout provides practice with basic division facts in the context of a simple but engaging strategy game.

Frequency

One day per week

Skills & Concepts

★ developing efficient strategies for doing basic division facts

You'll need

★ Introducing Division Capture (Overhead NC 8.4)

★ Division Capture Instructions (Number Corner Student Book, page 85)

★ Division Capture Game Sheets 1–3 (Number Corner Student Book, pages 86, 88, and 92)

★ 1 die numbered 1–6

★ 2 dice, one marked 1–6 and the other 4–9, for each pair of students

★ half-class set of calculators

★ overhead marking pens in two different colors

★ colored pencils

In the last two months' worth of Computational Fluency Workouts, students will play partner games that provide practice with basic facts. This month features Division Capture, a game in which partners take turns rolling a die and using the number that comes up to complete one of 20 division equations on a grid. Each partner uses a different color to write their numbers on the grid, and once all the equations are completed, players seek out any equations they completed that fall in a row, either vertically, horizontally, or diagonally. Each player earns a point for any 3 equations in a row and 2 points for any 4 equations in a row.

··

Week 1 Introducing Division Capture

Begin the first workout by explaining that this month students will play a new game called Division Capture. After playing a demonstration game with you at the overhead today, they will play in pairs for the rest of the month. Then display the text at the top of the Introducing Division Capture overhead. Read the game rules out loud to the class, and ask students to choose a pen color for the class and a different color for you. Fill in the boxes on the overhead to show which colors you'll be using. Then take turns with a volunteer rolling the die to determine whether you or the students will go first.

Computational Fluency Divison Capture (cont.)

Regardless of whether you or the students go first, once the number is rolled, ask students to study the 20 equations on the grid quietly and then raise their hands when they have found one or more that will work. Give students plenty of time so that nearly everyone has a chance to find an equation that will work, and let them know that there will be more than one equation that can be completed with this number. (There will be between 2 and 4 equations on the grid that can be completed with any number on the die.) When students identify the equations that would work with this number, ask them to explain how they know that the number will make the equation true.

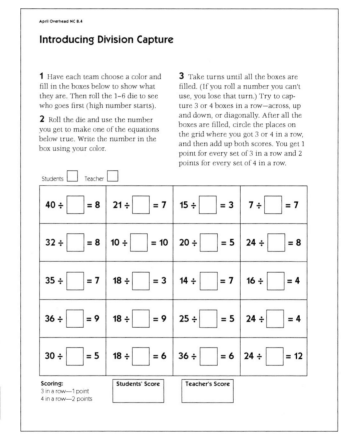

Teacher *I rolled a 5. Which equations can I complete by writing a 5 in the box? I'm going to ask that we all study the game board in silence and when you see several equations that would work, just raise your hand. When I see lots of hands, I'll call on people to share their ideas. ...*

Sage *Five would work in that one in the top row that says, "15 divided by box equals 3." Then it would be 15 ÷ 5 = 3, and I know that's true because 3 × 5 = 15.*

Keith *I see another one that would work. If you put the 5 in the very first box at the top, the sentence would say, "40 ÷ 5 = 8." I know it works because 8 × 5 = 40.*

Computational Fluency Divison Capture (cont.)

Susie *You could also use it for 25 ÷ 5 = 5 or 35 ÷ 5 = 7.*

Teacher *Are there any other places 5 would work as a divisor to complete the equation? No? So there are 4 possibilities. Which one should I choose?*

Students *The one in the top corner!*
Do 25 ÷ 5 = 5. I like that one.
It doesn't really matter right now.
You should choose one kind of in the middle so you'll have a better chance of getting others that line up with it later. I learned that from playing tic-tac-toe with my big brother.

Take turns rolling and recording with the class, and have a different student roll and record for the class each time it is their turn. Continue to give students time to think carefully about their choice of equation, especially toward the middle of the game when they will need to strategize in order to capture adjacent equations and block you from capturing adjacent equations. If you or the student rolls a number that can't be used, play passes to the other player. Toward the end of the game, you may have to pass the die back and forth a number of times until you or they are able to capture the last few equations.

When all 20 equations have been completed, ask a student volunteer to circle in their pen color any equations captured by the class that fall 3 or 4 in a row. Do the same for yourself using your pen color, and then have students use the scoring guide at the bottom of the overhead to calculate both scores.

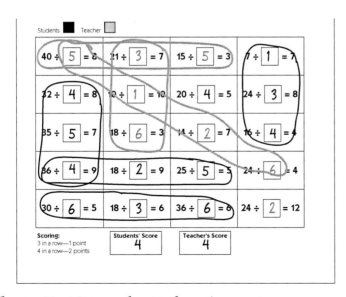

Students *Hey! It turned out to be a tie game!*
I thought we were going to lose when Mrs. MacIntosh got 24 ÷ 6 and it gave her 4 in a row.
We really lucked out when we got 36 ÷ 4 because that gave us 3 in a row in 2 directions.

Computational Fluency Divison Capture (cont.)

Note *Don't erase this overhead until after the next Computational Fluency Work-out. Displaying the completed game board next week will help you review the game before students play on their own in pairs.*

Weeks 2–4 Playing Division Capture

Open the second Computational Fluency Workout by quickly reviewing Division Capture. Display the completed overhead from the first week and have students read the game instructions on page 85 in their Number Corner Student Books.

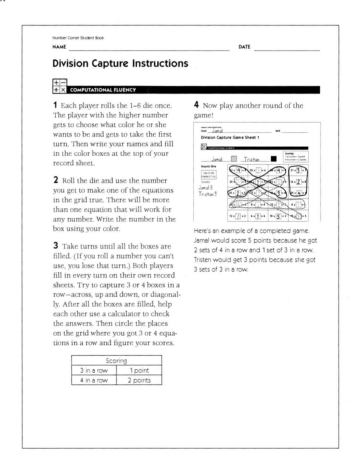

Make sure students see that there are three game sheets in their Student Books, and that each sheet has room for them to play two rounds. The third page features two challenge rounds that require a die marked 4–9 instead of 1–6. The first two sheets provide practice with division facts through $54 \div 6$, and the last sheet includes facts through $81 \div 9$. Even fourth graders who are quite fluent with their basic division facts will find the game strategies engaging, but you might encourage such students to start with the challenge version of the game on page 92 and possibly go on to design and use their own game boards.

April Problem Solving

PROBLEM SOLVING

Multiplication & Division Story Problems, Area, Perimeter & Fractions

STUDENT BOOK

Overview

This month's Problem Solving pages continue to offer multi-step problems. Two of the problems involve adding fractions with like denominators, and one challenges students to find the perimeter of 2 different rectangles based on information about one side and the area. Many involve 2-digit-by-1-digit multiplication or division, offering the opportunity to engage students in conversation about increasingly efficient and insightful ways to solve these computations.

Frequency

One day per week

Skills & Concepts

★ adding and subtracting 2- and 3-digit numbers with and without regrouping

★ multiplying and dividing multiples of 10 or 100

★ using different models of division to solve problems

★ multiplying and dividing 2- and 3-digit numbers by 1-digit numbers

★ adding commonly used fractions

★ developing strategies for finding the perimeter and area of rectangles

★ selecting methods and tools appropriate to a particular context for operations with whole numbers

★ solving multi-step story problems using a variety of efficient paper/pencil and mental strategies

You'll need

★ April Problem Solving Sheets 1–4 (Overheads NC 8.5 and 8.9–8.11)

★ Problem Solving Solution Page (Blackline NC 6.5, 4 class sets, optional)

★ April Problem Strips, pages 1 and 2 (Blacklines NC 8.9 and 8.10, class set cut into strips along dotted lines, optional)

★ April Problem Solving Sheets 1–4 (Number Corner Student Book, pages 82, 87, 89, and 93)

★ base ten pieces and/or Base Ten Grid Paper (Blackline NC 1.9, and/or NC 8.7 run as needed)

★ piece of paper to mask parts of the overhead

★ overhead pens and a few blank transparencies

....

Note If you want students to communicate their thinking and solutions in a more structured fashion, you can give each student a Problem Solving Solution Page and a set of problem strips each week.

....

Problem Solving Multiplication & Division ... Area, Perimeter & Fractions (cont.)

It is important that students specify the unit of measure when reporting their answers. Before they begin working on the first page of problems, emphasize that they must include the units when reporting their answers, and as you circulate to see how students are working, remind them to include the units if you notice that they are not.

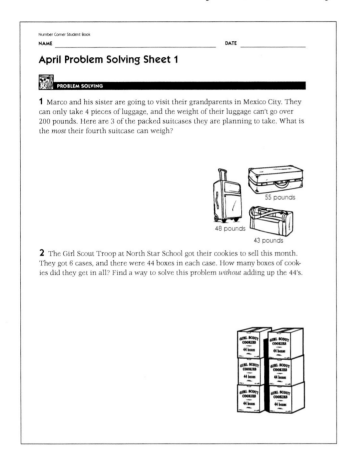

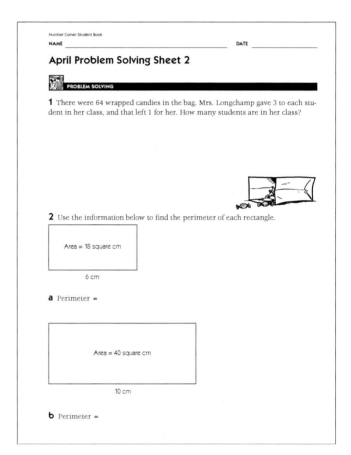

Some of the problems this month also explicitly ask students to use and communicate computational methods other than the tried and true. For example, two questions ask students to solve multiplication computations with strategies that do not involve repeated addition, a popular and reliable, although not efficient, method with fourth graders. Alternative strategies include sketching the problem on Base Ten Grid Paper or as an open array, as shown on the next page. Students might also use multiplication facts they already know to help solve the problem. A student who computes 8×32 by reasoning that 8×30 is 240 and 8×2 is 16, so the total is 256, is demonstrating good multiplicative thinking, number sense, and efficiency. These partial products (8×30 and 8×2) are easy to see and understand when 8×32 is shown as a rectangular array, although some students may not draw a visual model.

Problem Solving Multiplication & Division ... Area, Perimeter & Fractions (cont.)

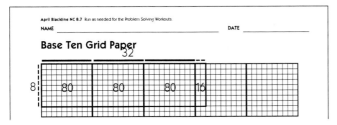

8 × 32 shown on Base Ten Grid Paper

8 × 32 sketched as an open array

If a student uses the standard multiplication algorithm, which is a valid method, be sure they understand what they're doing by asking them to explain how they completed the calculation. If a student is unable to identify the place values of the numbers she is "carrying over," as shown in the example below, ask her to use a second method to calculate the product.

"8 times 2 is 16. Carry the 1. 8 times 3 is 24. Add 1 and that makes 25. So it's 256."

You may also need to press students to find more efficient strategies for solving the first problem on the second sheet. (There were 64 wrapped candies in the bag. Mrs. Longchamp gave 3 to each student in her class, and that left 1 for her. How many students are in her class?) Some students may want to draw or make groups of 3 until they reach 64, but challenge them to find a way to do it that does not involve drawing out each piece of candy and counting groups of 3. If no one has any ideas about how to do this, you might need to encourage them to break the number 64 into more manageable pieces, such as 60 + 4. From there, some students will see that 60 ÷ 3 = 20, and 4 ÷ 3 = 1 R1. Therefore, there are 21 students in the class. While you don't want to communicate that there is only one way to solve a problem, you will need

Problem Solving Multiplication & Division … Area, Perimeter & Fractions (cont.)

to work with students to evaluate the different possibilities and encourage them to continue moving in the direction of efficiency and elegance.

As in months past, make time to discuss the students' solutions and methods for those problems that proved most interesting or challenging, and encourage them to take the lead in these discussions. You may find that if students are having trouble generating alternative strategies for some problems, it is helpful to reconvene the class while they are still working so that they can share ideas and get inspiration from each other in order to develop a variety of strategies for a given problem.

Number Corner Student Book
NAME _____ DATE _____

April Problem Solving Sheet 3

PROBLEM SOLVING

1 It takes Ravi 15 minutes to ride $2\frac{1}{4}$ miles on his bike. At this rate, how far can he ride in 1 hour?

2 Apples are 5 for a dollar. How many can you buy with $2.40?

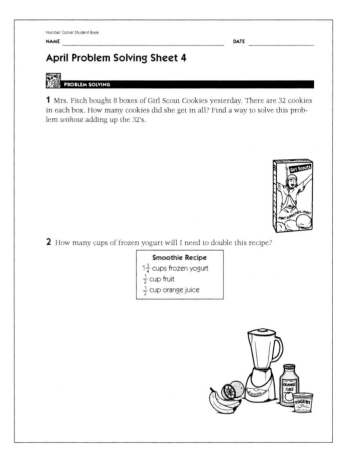

Number Corner Student Book
NAME _____ DATE _____

April Problem Solving Sheet 4

PROBLEM SOLVING

1 Mrs. Fitch bought 8 boxes of Girl Scout Cookies yesterday. There are 32 cookies in each box. How many cookies did she get in all? Find a way to solve this problem *without* adding up the 32's.

2 How many cups of frozen yogurt will I need to double this recipe?

Smoothie Recipe
$1\frac{3}{4}$ cups frozen yogurt
$\frac{1}{2}$ cup fruit
$\frac{1}{2}$ cup orange juice

April Number Line

Decimal Draw

Overview

Students play a whole-class game in which they order decimal numbers along a number line and then add them. This workout is meant to be a review of decimal numbers, and of the connection between fractions and decimal numbers.

Frequency

Once a week

Skills & Concepts

★ modeling, recognizing, and ordering decimals

★ recognizing equivalent forms of common fractions and decimals to hundredths

★ locating decimals to hundredths on a number line

★ adding decimals (tenths and hundredths)

STUDENT BOOK

You'll need

★ Decimal Draw (Overhead NC 8.6)

★ Decimal Draw Cards, pages 1 and 2 (Overheads NC 8.7 and 8.8, see Advance Preparation)

★ Decimal Draw Game Sheets 1 and 2 (Number Corner Student Book, pages 83 and 90)

★ overhead pens in red and black

★ red pencils

....

Advance Preparation Before the first Number Line Workout this month, cut apart the overhead Decimal Draw Cards and then store them in a small, sturdy manila envelope or in a resealable plastic bag for repeated use this month and in future years.

....

A Summary of Decimal Draw

To play Decimal Draw, you and the students will take turns drawing cards that each feature one of three formats: visual models of decimals, decimal fractions, and common fractions such as $^1/_4$ and $^1/_2$ that are easily converted to decimal form.

You and the students will record the number shown on each card as both a fraction and a decimal along the 0–1 number line. (You will record on the overhead and they will record in their Student Books.) The card shown above at the far left, for instance, would be recorded as both $^{33}/_{100}$ and 0.33. You and the students will record your numbers along the same line. Yours will be in black and theirs will be in red. After you have each taken four turns, students will find the sum of your numbers and theirs. The high score wins.

Number Line Decimal Draw (cont.)

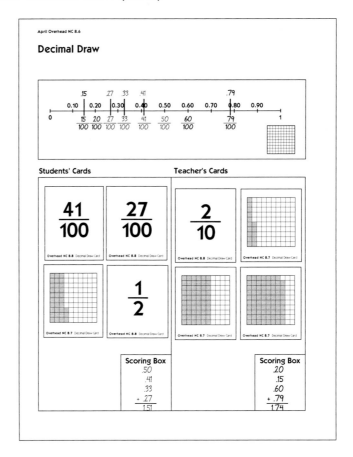

....

Week 1 Introducing Decimal Draw

To introduce Decimal Draw, display the Decimal Draw overhead and have students open their Student Books to page 83. Also ask each student to get out a regular pencil and a red pencil. Explain that you're going to teach them a new game that you'll play together as a class a few times this month.

Before you get started, ask students to examine the number line at the top of page 83 and on the overhead, and then discuss their observations first in pairs and then as a class.

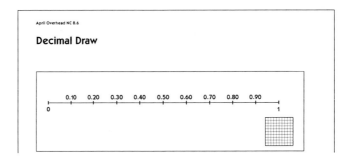

Students *It starts with 0 and only goes to 1.*
Those numbers in between are decimal numbers. See the decimal points?

Number Line Decimal Draw (cont.)

They look like bigger numbers, like 80 or 90, but the decimal point means they're less than 1.
You can only put small numbers on here, like half and things like that.
You can't have anything bigger than 1 on this line.
This is like the line last month, except there's no dollars.
But what's that thing at the end under the 1?
It's like a base ten mat.
Or a dollar mat on the money pieces.

Be sure students understand that the small array beneath the 1 is a visual model for 1, and ask them to identify the value of each small square within the array ($1/100$, since there are 100 small squares in the 1). If they haven't already, ask them to discuss the numbers between 0 and 1 shown on the line. For example, how is the number 0.50 read, and to which fractions is it equivalent? As they share the equivalencies, record them on the board (you won't have room on the overhead number line).

> **Teacher** *So what about these decimal numbers between 0 and 1? For example, how would you read this number, and can you think of any fractions it is equal to?* (pointing to 0.50)

> **Students** *It's point-five-oh.*
> *Hey, it's right in the middle, and I remember point-five is a half. So it's equal to $1/2$.*
> *Right, like 50 cents. That's half a dollar.*
> *If you colored in 50 of those tiny squares on the mat, it would be half.*
> *You can also say 50 over 100 for fifty-hundredths.*
> *Or 5 out of 10, remember?*
> *I don't get that.*
> *Well, remember point-five is the same as point-five-oh?*
> *If you colored it in on the mat, it would be 50 little squares, but that's also 5 columns of 10. Five-tenths, 5 out of 10.*

$$0.50 = \frac{1}{2} \qquad 0.50 = \frac{5}{10} \qquad 0.50 = \frac{50}{100}$$

After students have discussed the line, briefly explain how Decimal Draw is played and then invite a student volunteer to draw a card and set it on the students' side of the overhead. Ask students how the model or fraction on the card could be shown as a decimal fraction (some will already be in this form), recorded in decimal notation, and placed along the number line. When thinking about where to place it on the line, you may need to encourage them to think about it in relation to the decimals that have already been marked on the line.

Number Line Decimal Draw (cont.)

Teacher *Kathryn has selected one of the picture cards. What decimal fraction do you see pictured here? A decimal fraction is one where the denominator is a factor of 10, like 10 or 100.*

Students *There are 46 little boxes colored in on that card.*
It's like 46.
But 46 is way more than 1. How can we put that number on the line?
But, remember? One is a whole big square of 100 of those little boxes.
So this is only part of 1.

Teacher *What fraction or part of 1 does this show?*

Students *It's not quite a half, but almost.*
It's 46 out of 100, because 46 of those little boxes are colored in.
It's ⁴⁶/₁₀₀.
It's kind of like 46 cents!

Teacher *Let's record the fraction ⁴⁶/₁₀₀ under the line. Where does it belong?*

Kathryn *Almost right by the middle mark on the line. Can I show?*

Teacher *Sure! Actually, I'd like all of you to make a mark along the number line in your book to show where ⁴⁶/₁₀₀ would go. Also write that fraction below the line, like this. Please use a red pencil so you can re-member that this is your number and not mine. We'll write my numbers in regular pencil. ... Mathematicians have invented a shorthand nota-tion for ⁴⁶/₁₀₀. Let's write our fraction in this special decimal form too. Does anyone remember what it is?*

Connor *I think it's point-four-six. The point means that it's less than 1. I remember that from when we learned about decimals.*

Teacher *Talk to your partner to decide if you agree with Connor. How can you prove your thinking using the picture?*

The visual model for decimals makes the connection between decimal frac-tions and decimal notation very explicit. On the card selected by the students above, for instance, students can see the 0.4 (four-tenths) in the four strips, each of which represents one-tenth. The 0.06 is represented by the six small squares that are each worth one-hundredth.

Number Line Decimal Draw (cont.)

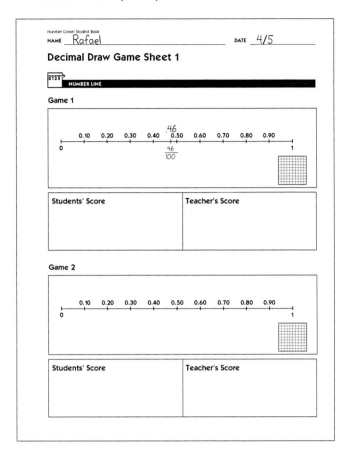

Now draw a card for yourself and set it on your side of the overhead for all to see. Ask students how the number or model on your card be shown in the form of a decimal fraction and a decimal. The discussion will vary depending on the type of card you've drawn, but each format offers its own opportunities to help students establish and reinforce the connections between decimal fractions, decimals, and common fractions.

Students *It's ¹/₄. That's less than 1.*
I know where it would go on the line! Halfway between 0 and the half mark.
One-fourth is the same as 0.25.
How do you know?
Because it's the same as a quarter!
One fourth is the same as ²⁵/₁₀₀. Remember from when were collecting quarters a few months ago?

Number Line Decimal Draw (cont.)

After some discussion, record your number as a decimal fraction and a decimal using the black overhead pen. Have students do the same on their game sheets, using a regular pencil to distinguish between their numbers and yours.

Continue in this way until you have both had four turns. Then have students find the sum of their numbers and the sum of your numbers while you record their thinking at the overhead. Discuss the placement of the decimal point in the final answer as necessary. The team with the higher score wins.

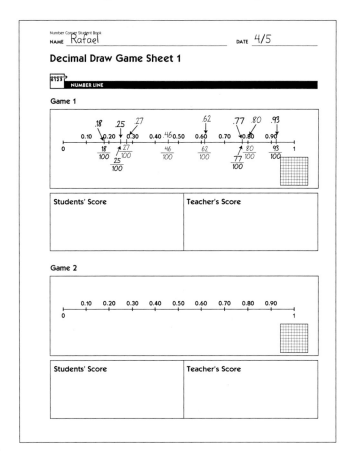

Save this completed overhead for use in the second Number Line Workout. You can use it to review with students how the game is played.

Weeks 2–4 Playing Decimal Draw

Play the game at least one time each in the next three Number Line Workouts. At the beginning of the second workout, you may find it helpful to post the completed overhead from the first week and use it to review how the game is played.

April Answer Keys

 ANSWER KEY

Number Corner Student Book

page 82, April Problem Solving Sheet 1

1 54 lbs. at most, Students' strategies will vary. Examples:

example 1:

80 ⟍ 11
48 ⟍
43 ⟍
55

$80 + 11 = 91$
$91 + 55 = 146$
$200 - 146 = 54$

example 2:

$$48 + 43 + 55$$
$$+ 2 \ \ + 3 \ \ - 5$$
$$\overline{50 + 46 + 50} = 146$$
$$200 - 146 = 54$$

2 264 boxes, Students' strategies will vary. Examples:

example 1:

44 × 6 = (44 × 2) × 3 = 88 + 88 + 88 = 240 + 24
= 264

example 2:

44 × 6 = 40 × 6 + 4 × 6 = 240 + 24 = 264

page 84, A Closer Look at the Perimeter Pattern

1 Students' equations will vary. Examples are shown below.

Date	Shape Name	Equation to Show How You Found the Perimeter	Perimeter (cm)
1	Equilateral Triangle	1 × 3 = 3	3 cm
2	Rectangle	1 + 1 + 2 + 2 = 6	6 cm
3	Pentagon	1 × 5 = 5	5 cm
4	Isosceles Triangle	3 + 3 + 2 = 8	8 cm
5	Trapezoid	1 + 1 + 2 + 3 = 7	7 cm
6	Pentagon	2 × 5 = 10	10 cm
7	Equilateral Triangle	3 × 3 = 9	9 cm
8	Square	3 × 3 = 9 & 3 × 4 = 12	12 cm
9	Pentagon	3 + 2 + 2 + 3 + 1 = 11	11 cm
10	Isosceles Triangle	5 + 5 + 4 = 14	14 cm

2 Students' observations will vary. Examples:

• *The pattern goes odd, even, odd, even, and on like that.*

• *First it adds 3 and then takes away 1. That pattern repeats over and over.*

• *It goes triangle, quadrilateral, pentagon, and then that repeats.*

• *The quadrilaterals are different things. One is a square, one is a rectangle, and one is a trapezoid.*

• *Some of the pentagons have equal sides and some don't.*

• *The triangles go equilateral, isosceles, equilateral, isosceles.*

• *The quadrilaterals go rectangle, not rectangle, rectangle (a square is a rectangle).*

• *The pentagons go regular, regular, not regular.*

page 87, April Problem Solving Sheet 2

1 21 students, Students' strategies will vary. Examples:

example 1:

64 – 1 = 63 for the kids

63 candies ÷ 3 candies/kid = 21 kids

example 2:

I know 3 × 20 is 60. 3 more makes 63, so 21 × 3 = 63. So 21 kids get 3 candies and then 1 for the teacher. 21 kids in the class.

2 a 18 cm, Students' strategies will vary. Example:

18 ÷ 6 = 3

6 × 2 + 3 × 2 = 12 + 6 = 18 cm

b 28 cm, Students' strategies will vary. Example:

40 ÷ 10 = 4

10 × 2 + 4 × 2 = 20 + 8 = 28

page 89, April Problem Solving Sheet 3

1 9 miles, Students' strategies will vary. Example:

15 mins.	15 mins.
$2\frac{1}{4}$ miles	$2\frac{1}{4}$ miles

In 30 mins., he can go 4 and ½ miles. So in 60 minutes, he can go 8 plus 1 = 9 miles.

ANSWER KEY

Number Corner Student Book (cont.)

page 89, April Problem Solving Sheet 3 (cont.)

2 12 apples, Students' strategies will vary. Example: *With $2, he can get 10 apples. $1 ÷ 5 = 20¢, so each apple is 20¢. So with 40 more cents, he can get 2 more apples. 12 apples altogether.*

page 91, More Perimeters & a Triangle Problem

1 Students' equations will vary. Examples are shown below.

Date	Shape Name	Equation to Show How You Found the Perimeter	Perimeter (cm)
17	Trapezoid	3 + 5 + 3 + 8 = 19	19 cm
18	Pentagon	6 + 6 + 3 + 4 + 3 = 22	22 cm
19	Equilateral Triangle	7 × 3 = 21	21 cm
20	Rhombus	6 × 4 = 24	24 cm
21	Pentagon	5 + 3 + 3 + 4 + 8 = 23	23 cm

2 Students' triangles will vary. Examples:
2, 12, and 12 cm; 7, 9.5, and 9.5 cm; 12, 7, and 7 cm

page 93, April Problem Solving Sheet 4

1 256 cookies, Students' strategies will vary. Example:
$32 \times 8 = (32 + 32) \times 4 = 64 \times 4 = 240 + 16 = 256$

2 $3\frac{1}{2}$ cups of yogurt, Students' strategies will vary. Example:
$1\frac{3}{4} + 1\frac{3}{4} = 2 + \frac{3}{4} + \frac{1}{4} + \frac{2}{4} = 2 + 1 + \frac{2}{4} = 3\frac{2}{4}$ or $3\frac{1}{2}$

May & June Overhead HC 9.2

Trip Mileage Record Sheet page 1 of 2

CALENDAR COLLECTOR

Day	Start Point	End Point	Miles Traveled This Day	Total Miles	Show Your Work
1	Anchorage, AK	San Francisco, CA	2,010 mi.	2,010 mi.	
2	San Francisco, CA	Reno, NV	230	2,240 mi.	
3	Reno, NV	Portland, OR	580	2,820 mi.	
4	Portland, OR	Seattle, WA	170	2,990 mi.	
5	Seattle, WA	Boise, ID	501	3,491 mi.	
6	Boise, ID	Missoula, MT	369	3,860 mi.	
7	Missoula, MT	Billings, MT	344	4,204 mi.	
8	Billings, MT	Cheyenne, WY	456	4,660 mi.	
9	Cheyenne, WY	Denver, CO	101	4,761 mi.	
10	Denver, CO	Rapid City, SD	407	5,168 mi.	
11	Rapid City, SD	Sioux Falls, SD	347	5,515 mi.	
12	Sioux Falls, SD	Lincoln, NE	236	5,751 mi.	
13	Lincoln, NE	Wichita, KS	276	6,027 mi.	
14	Wichita, KS	Oklahoma City, OK	160	6,187 mi.	
15	Oklahoma City, OK	Dallas, TX	207	6,394 mi.	
16	Dallas, TX	Houston, TX	239	6,633 mi.	

May & June Calendar Record Sheet

Date	Coordinate	Direction of the drive	Destination (name of the city and the state)
5/1	A,7	—	San Francisco, California
5/2	B,8	N.E.	Reno, Nevada
5/3	B,10	N.	Portland, Oregon
5/4	B,11	N.E.	Seattle, Washington
5/5	C,9	S.E.	Boise, Idaho
5/6	D,10	N.E.	Missoula, Montana
5/7	F,9	S.E.	Billings, Montana
5/8	F,7	S.E.	Cheyenne, Wyoming
5/9	F,7	S.	Denver, Colorado
5/10	G,8	N.E.	Rapid City, South Dakota
5/11	I,8	S.E.	Sioux Falls, South Dakota
5/12	I,7	S.	Lincoln, Nebraska
5/13	I,5	S.W.	Wichita, Kansas
5/14	I,5	S.W.	Oklahoma City, Oklahoma
5/15	I,4	S.	Dallas, Texas
5/16	I,2	S.E.	Houston, Texas

May & June Overhead HC 9.1

Continental U.S. Map

CALENDAR GRID

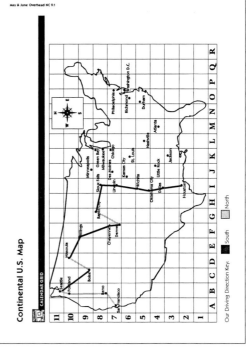

Our Driving Direction Key: ■ South   ▨ North

Calendar Grid

May

Sunday	Monday	Tuesday	Wednesday	Thursday	Friday	Saturday
A, 7 **1**	B, 8 **2**	B, 10 **3**	B, 11 **4**	C, 9 **5**	D, 10 **6**	F, 9 **7**
F, 7 **8**	F, 7 **9**	G, 8 **10**	I, 8 **11**	I, 7 **12**	I, 5 **13**	I, 5 **14**
I, 4 **15**	I, 2 **16**					

Number Corner Student Book

NAME _____ DATE _____

May & June Problem Solving Sheet 1

PROBLEM SOLVING

1 Mina's family is driving from Seattle, Washington, to Boise, Idaho. The distance is 501 miles. They have 248 miles left to drive. How many miles have they driven so far?

2a It takes 1 gallon of gas for the family's rental car to drive 30 miles. How many gallons of gas will it take to drive from Durham, North Carolina, to Richmond, Virginia, which is a distance of about 150 miles?

b Gas costs $2.98 a gallon in that part of the country. How much will the gas for this part of the trip cost? Find a way to solve this problem without just adding $2.98 over and over again.

Problem Solving

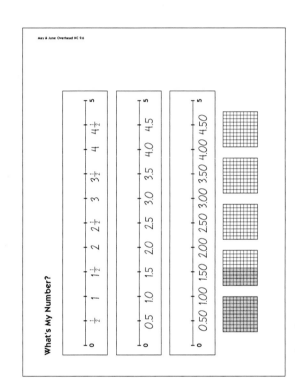

May & June Overhead NC 9.6

What's My Number?

Number Line

May & June Overhead NC 9.4

Roll 5

Teacher | Target Number: **20** | | **Students**

Round 1
Target Number: **20**
5 Numbers Rolled: **2** **1** **6** **4** **4**
My Equation: **((1 + 6) × 4) − (2 × 4)**
Points scored this round: **5**

Round 2
Target Number
5 Numbers Rolled
My Equation
Points scored this round

Round 3
Target Number
5 Numbers Rolled
My Equation
Points scored this round

Round 4
Target Number
5 Numbers Rolled
My Equation
Points scored this round

Total
Teacher's Total Score: _____

Students

Target Number
5 Numbers Rolled
My Equation
Points scored this round

Target Number
5 Numbers Rolled
My Equation
Points scored this round

Target Number
5 Numbers Rolled
My Equation
Points scored this round

Target Number
5 Numbers Rolled
My Equation
Points scored this round

Students' Total Score: _____

Computational Fluency

What's Going to Happen in May & June?

The Calendar Grid, Calendar Collector, and Problem Solving Workouts this month revolve around an imaginary driving trip made by a family who flies from their home in Alaska to California, rents a car, and travels across the continental United States over the course of a month.

The Computational Fluency Workout features a game that can be played as a class or in pairs to help students develop fluency with all four basic operations, while the Number Line Workouts help students continue to develop understandings of fractions and decimals. This month also features the final skills checkup of the year, as well as Support Activities that be used to strengthen specific skills over the summer.

Calendar Grid

The pattern this month tracks the course of an imaginary family who flies from their home in Alaska to San Francisco and then rents a car and drives across the continental United States. Each calendar marker shows coordinates that identify the family's destination city for that day. Students record each step of the trip on a record sheet, and once a week, they trace the route on a map in the Number Corner Student Book, searching for trends and patterns that will enable them to predict the family's upcoming destinations.

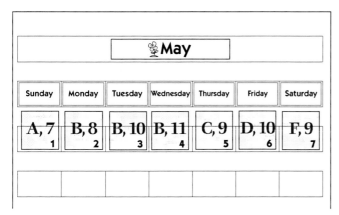

May & June Calendar Record Sheet			
Date	Coordinate	Direction of the drive	Destination (name of the city and the state)
5/1	A, 7	———	San Francisco, California
5/2	B, 8	N.E.	Reno, Nevada
5/3	B, 10	N.	Portland, Oregon
5/4	B, 11	N.E.	Seattle, Washington
5/5	C, 9	S.E.	Boise, Idaho
5/6	D, 10	N.E.	Missoula, Montana
5/7	F, 9	S.E	Billings, Montana

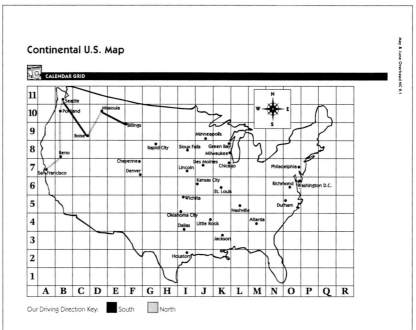

Calendar Collector

This month's Calendar Collector is a companion piece to the Calendar Grid. Students keep a running total of the number of miles the family drives each day as they make their way across the country. At the beginning of the month, the class estimates how many miles the family will travel in all, and students are encouraged to revise their estimates each week as more information is collected. The workout is meant to provide points of reference for long distances measured in miles, as well as practice making calculations with up to 5-digit numbers.

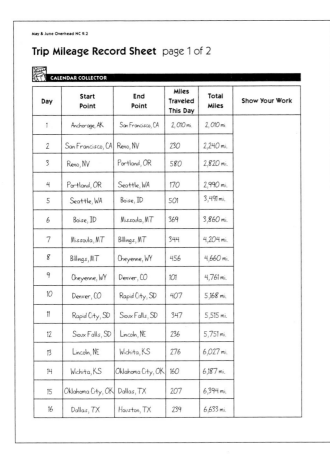

May & June Overhead NC 9.2

Trip Mileage Record Sheet page 1 of 2

CALENDAR COLLECTOR

Day	Start Point	End Point	Miles Traveled This Day	Total Miles	Show Your Work
1	Anchorage, AK	San Francisco, CA	2,010 mi.	2,010 mi.	
2	San Francisco, CA	Reno, NV	230	2,240 mi.	
3	Reno, NV	Portland, OR	580	2,820 mi.	
4	Portland, OR	Seattle, WA	170	2,990 mi.	
5	Seattle, WA	Boise, ID	501	3,491 mi.	
6	Boise, ID	Missoula, MT	369	3,860 mi.	
7	Missoula, MT	Billings, MT	344	4,204 mi.	
8	Billings, MT	Cheyenne, WY	456	4,660 mi.	
9	Cheyenne, WY	Denver, CO	101	4,761 mi.	
10	Denver, CO	Rapid City, SD	407	5,168 mi.	
11	Rapid City, SD	Sioux Falls, SD	347	5,515 mi.	
12	Sioux Falls, SD	Lincoln, NE	236	5,751 mi.	
13	Lincoln, NE	Wichita, KS	276	6,027 mi.	
14	Wichita, KS	Oklahoma City, OK	160	6,187 mi.	
15	Oklahoma City, OK	Dallas, TX	207	6,394 mi.	
16	Dallas, TX	Houston, TX	239	6,633 mi.	

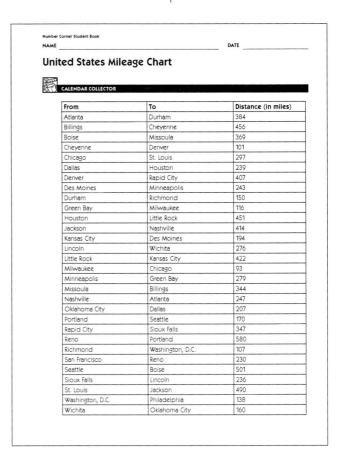

Number Corner Student Book

NAME _____ DATE _____

United States Mileage Chart

CALENDAR COLLECTOR

From	To	Distance (in miles)
Atlanta	Durham	384
Billings	Cheyenne	456
Boise	Missoula	369
Cheyenne	Denver	101
Chicago	St. Louis	297
Dallas	Houston	239
Denver	Rapid City	407
Des Moines	Minneapolis	243
Durham	Richmond	150
Green Bay	Milwaukee	116
Houston	Little Rock	451
Jackson	Nashville	414
Kansas City	Des Moines	194
Lincoln	Wichita	276
Little Rock	Kansas City	422
Milwaukee	Chicago	93
Minneapolis	Green Bay	279
Missoula	Billings	344
Nashville	Atlanta	247
Oklahoma City	Dallas	207
Portland	Seattle	170
Rapid City	Sioux Falls	347
Reno	Portland	580
Richmond	Washington, D.C.	107
San Francisco	Reno	230
Seattle	Boise	501
Sioux Falls	Lincoln	236
St. Louis	Jackson	490
Washington, D.C.	Philadelphia	138
Wichita	Oklahoma City	160

Computational Fluency

The last Computational Fluency Workout of the year is the game of Roll 5, which was offered as a challenge option in January. In the game, a player rolls two dice and multiplies the two numbers that come up to establish a target number. Then the player rolls 5 dice and uses as many of the 5 numbers as possible to multiply, divide, add, or subtract to get to the target number, earning a point for each number used. After three rounds, the player with the most points wins. This game provides plenty of practice using all four operations in a problem-solving context and can be played either as a whole group or in partners or small teams.

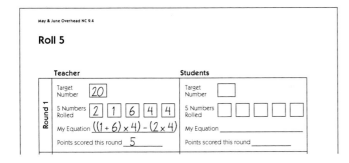

May & June Overhead NC 9.4

Roll 5

Round 1

	Teacher	Students
Target Number	20	
5 Numbers Rolled	2 1 6 4 4	
My Equation	$((1 + 6) \times 4) - (2 \times 4)$	
Points scored this round	5	

$$(6 + 4) \times (4 - 2) = 20 \qquad \text{4 points}$$
$$(6 + 4) \times (4 - 2) \times 1 = 20 \qquad \text{5 points}$$
$$((4 \times 4) + 6) - (2 \times 1) = 20 \qquad \text{5 points}$$
$$((1 + 6) \times 4) - (2 \times 4) = 20 \qquad \text{5 points}$$

Problem Solving

Like the Calendar Grid and the Calendar Collector, this month's problems feature the imaginary family as they travel across the United States. The computational focus is multiplication and division, although there is some multi-digit addition and subtraction as well. Most of the problems are multi-step and feature opportunities to use such clearly defined strategies as drawing a picture, making a table, using logical reasoning, simplifying, or guessing and checking to make the computation easier.

Number Line

This month's Number Line Workout returns to the game of What's My Number?, which requires students to read, order, and compare whole numbers, fractions, decimals, and mixed numbers between 0 and 5. The class is divided into two teams to play What's My Number?. Each team takes turns guessing the teacher's secret number: a number between 0 and 5 expressed as a mixed number or decimal number to the tenths or hundredths place. The teacher indicates whether each guess is greater or less than the secret number, so the range of possibilities is narrowed with each guess. The first team to guess the number exactly wins the game.

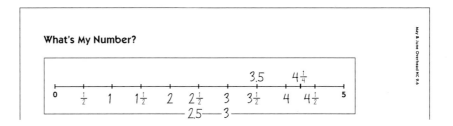

After each team has made 2 guesses, the range of possibilities has been narrowed to between 3 and 3.5.

Assessment & Support Activities

This month includes the last of four quarterly skills checkups. The May/June checkup focuses on basic multiplication and division facts; comprehension of the operations of multiplication and division; multi-digit addition, subtraction, multiplication, and division; identifying multiples and factors; ordering whole numbers; reading and interpreting bar graphs, pictographs, and circle graphs; probability; and fractions and decimals. This checkup, like the other three checkups this year, is optional. However, it can provide a good summary of what students know and can do with regard to key math skills at this point in the school year, and also provides an opportunity to practice test-taking skills.

We suggest that you administer the checkup at the end of the month, or even very early in June, as it may provide information that is timely and useful to you in writing fourth-quarter report cards. The results can also help you assign Support Activities as needed for children to work on over the summer.

Planning for May & June

You can use the planning guide below as shown or adapt it to fit the needs of your students and schedule.

MAY & JUNE PLANNING GUIDE							
Key ★ = Discuss ☆ = Update SB = Number Corner Student Book	MON	TUES	WED	THURS	FRI	SB	
Calendar Grid, pp. 343–348 Map Coordinates • locating and identifying coordinates on maps • identifying directions on a map • using a map scale to figure distances	★	☆	☆	☆	★	pp. 94, 101, 102, 104 & 105	
Calendar Collector, pp. 349–353 Collecting Trip Miles • multi-digit addition • reading and constructing tables and graphs • making and refining estimates on the basis of a growing collection of data	☆	★	☆	☆	☆	pp. 95–97 & 107	
Computational Fluency, pp. 354–356 Roll 5 • adding, subtracting, multiplying, and dividing numbers using mental strategies			★				
Problem Solving, pp. 357–359 Travel Puzzlers • multi-digit addition, subtraction, multiplication, and division • solving multi-step story problems using a variety of strategies				★		pp. 98–100, 103 & 106	
Number Line, pp. 360–364 What's My Number? • reading, ordering, and recognizing equivalent forms of common fractions and decimals • locating common fractions and decimals to hundredths on a number line	☆	☆	☆	☆	★		
Assessment, pp. 365–368 Number Corner Checkup 4	Give this assessment during the last week of May or first week of June (Blacklines NC A 9.1–9.6)						
Support Activities, pp. 368 and 369 Multiplying and Dividing 2-Digit by 1-Digit Numbers, Decimals to Hundredths, Relating Decimals to Fractions	Provide for use over the summer, after administering Number Corner Checkup 4. (Blacklines NC S 26.1–29.7)						

Materials You'll Need for May & June

MANIPULATIVES & MATERIALS

Manipulatives
- Calendar Grid pocket chart
- 1 die numbered 0–5 for each pair of students
- 2 dice numbered 1–6 for each pair of students
- 2 dice numbered 4–9 for each pair of students
- calculators

Number Corner Calendar Markers
- Day, Month, and Year markers
- Map Coordinates calendar markers

General Materials
- classroom map of the United States or world (optional)
- overhead pens in black, red, and blue
- a few blank overhead transparencies
- colored pencils
- marking pens in several different colors
- chart paper (optional)
- scratch paper
- a piece of paper to mask parts of the overhead when necessary
- rulers

BLACKLINES & OVERHEADS

Number Corner Overheads
NC 9.1	Continental U.S. Map
NC 9.2 & 9.3	Trip Mileage Record Sheet, pages 1 and 2
NC 9.4	Roll 5
NC 9.5	May & June Problem Solving Sheet 1
NC 9.6	What's My Number?
NC 9.7	May & June Problem Solving Sheet 2
NC 9.8	May & June Problem Solving Sheet 3
NC 9.9	May & June Problem Solving Sheet 4

Number Corner Blacklines
NC 1.1	Monthly Planner Template (1 copy, optional)
NC 6.5	Problem Solving Solution Page (4 class sets, optional)
NC 9.1 & 9.2	May & June Calendar Grid Record Sheet, pages 1 and 2
NC 9.3	Continental U.S. Map
NC 9.4 & 9.5	May & June Problem Strips, pages 1 and 2 (class set cut into sections, optional)

Number Corner Assessment Blacklines
NC A 9.1–9.6	Number Corner Checkup 4, pages 1–6 (class set)
NC A 9.7	Base Ten Grid Paper (class set)
NC A 9.8–9.10	Number Corner Checkup 4 Class Checklist, pages 1–3 (2 or 3 copies as needed, optional)

Number Corner Student Book
page 51	Roll 5
pages 52–54	Roll 5 Record Sheets, pages 1–3
page 94	Continental U.S. Map
page 95	United States Mileage Chart
pages 96 & 97	Trip Mileage Record Sheet, pages 1 and 2
page 98	Base Ten Grid Paper
page 99	May & June Problem Solving Sheet 1
page 100	May & June Problem Solving Sheet 2
pages 101 & 102	Looking Ahead & Making Predictions, pages 1 and 2
page 103	May & June Problem Solving Sheet 3
pages 104 & 105	Map Problems, pages 1 and 2
page 106	May & June Problem Solving Sheet 4
page 107	Graphing the Miles

ADVANCE PREPARATON

Calendar Grid
Run 1 copy each of Blacklines NC 9.1–9.3. Trim and glue the first two sheets together to form one long record sheet. Post the record sheet and the map on your calendar display board before the first Calendar Grid Workout this month.

May & June Calendar Grid

CALENDAR GRID

Map Coordinates

Overview

The final calendar pattern of the year features an imaginary driving trip made by a family that flies from their home in Anchorage, Alaska, to San Francisco, California, rents a car, and travels across the continental United States over the course of a month. The family heads for a new location each day, zigzagging their way eastward until they reach Philadelphia, Pennsylvania. Each new calendar marker identifies the destination of the family for that day by naming a coordinate that can be located on a map. Students make predictions about upcoming destinations and keep a mileage chart throughout the month.

Frequency

Update the Calendar Grid and record sheet each day, and share observations and predictions at least once a week.

Skills & Concepts

★ locating and identifying coordinates on maps

★ identifying directions on a map (North, South, East, and West)

★ using a map scale to figure distances

★ solving story problems using a variety of efficient strategies

★ accurately measuring length to the nearest centimeter

STUDENT BOOK

You'll need

★ Continental U.S. Map (Overhead NC 9.1)

★ May & June Calendar Grid Record Sheet, pages 1 and 2 (Blacklines NC 9.1 and 9.2, see Advance Preparation)

★ Continental U.S. Map (Blackline NC 9.3, see Advance Preparation)

★ Continental U.S. Map (Number Corner Student Book, page 94)

★ Looking Ahead & Making Predictions, pages 1 and 2 (Number Corner Student Book, pages 101 and 102)

★ Map Problems, pages 1 and 2 (Number Corner Student Book, pages 104 and 105)

★ Calendar Grid pocket chart

★ Day, Month, and Year markers

★ Map Coordinates calendar markers

★ classroom map of the United States or world (optional)

★ overhead pens in black and two other colors

★ rulers

★ colored pencils

Advance Preparation Run 1 copy each of Blacklines NC 9.1–9.3. Trim and glue the first two sheets together to form one long record sheet. Post the record sheet and the map on your calendar display board before the first Calendar Grid Workout this month.

Calendar Grid Map Coordinates (cont.)

....

Week 1 Introducing & Discussing the First Few Calendar Markers

Open the first workout this month by displaying the U.S. Map overhead. Ask students to study it quietly for a minute and then discuss their observations with a partner. After giving them some time to talk in pairs, explain that this map will help them follow the travels of an imaginary family—fourth grader, Mina, her fifth grade brother, Noah, Mom, and Dad—as they take a month-long driving trip across the United States. The family lives in Anchorage, Alaska, although Mom grew up in Seattle, Washington, and Dad in Philadelphia, Pennsylvania. Early the first morning of their trip, they flew from Anchorage to San Francisco, California, where they rented a car and stayed with friends that evening. The next day, they started the long drive, which your class will be able to follow with the help of the Calendar Grid markers each day.

If you have a classroom map of the world or the United States, display it so students can locate Alaska and see where it is in relation to the continental United States. Depending on students' geographical knowledge, you may also need to do a short geography review, perhaps even reminding students that they live in the United States, reviewing where the U.S. is located in relation to other countries like Canada and Mexico, and refreshing their understanding of the relationships between the states and the country as a whole (e.g., they live in the state of Washington, which is part of the country the United States of America).

Now ask a student to place the calendar markers up to and including today's in the Calendar Grid pocket chart. Leave the map displayed on the overhead or ask students to turn to their maps on page 94 in the Student Book. Ask students to converse in pairs and then share observations about the markers with the whole group. Specifically, ask them to discuss how the markers relate to the map.

Students will probably notice that each one identifies a coordinate box on the map that contains one or two cities. For example, in box A,7, they'll find San Francisco. You may need to explain that there are many other towns and cities in that region of the country. Only one has been shown on the map to help the class follow the travels of Mina and her family.

Calendar Grid Map Coordinates (cont.)

As students discuss their observations, work with their input to make entries
on the Calendar Grid Record Sheet for each marker posted so far (the first has
been provided to show the family's arrival in San Francisco). As you discuss
the direction the family drove each day, connect the dots on the overhead
map, using one color to show any move to the south and another to show any
move to the north. Be sure to record the color key on the overhead.

May & June Calendar Record Sheet			
Date	Coordinate	Direction of the drive	Destination (name of the city and the state)
5/1	A, 7	——————	San Francisco, California
5/2	B, 8	N.E.	Reno, Nevada

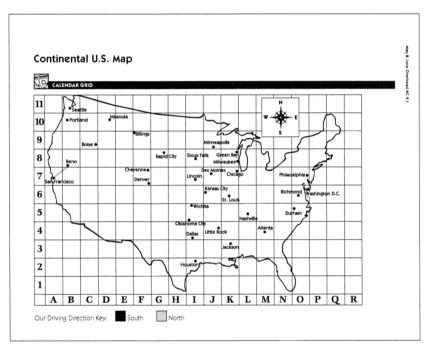

Finally, let students know that the calendar helper each day will need to post
the next marker on the grid, find the location indicated by that marker on the
blackline copy of the map you've posted, draw a line from the previous location to the next one using a ruler and the correct color, and make the entry
on the record sheet. The record sheet asks them to enter the state as well as
the city, so ask students to talk about how they could find out what state a
particular city is in if they don't already know. (If there is more than one city
in a box (e.g., F7), the north/south pattern will help students identify which
city to go to on a given day.)

Calendar Grid Map Coordinates (cont.)

....

Week 2 Tracking the Family's Travels & Making Predictions about Their Upcoming Destinations

Begin the second workout by displaying the U.S. Map overhead while students turn to the map on page 94 their Student Books. Work together to find the locations specified by the coordinates on the calendar markers that have been posted so far, including today's marker. Have students connect the dots from one location to the next, using the two colors to show movement to the south and north. Do the same on the overhead (the locations will already have been connected on the blackline map). Ask students to share observations about the markers, map, and the family's trip so far. Here are some questions to have them consider as the discussion proceeds:

- Can they detect any patterns in the markers or the route that is emerging on the map?
- Based on their route to date, where do students think the family will drive next?
- What states has the family traveled through so far?

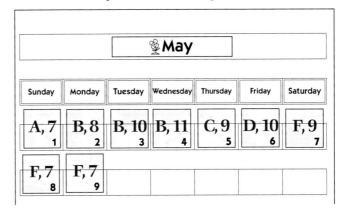

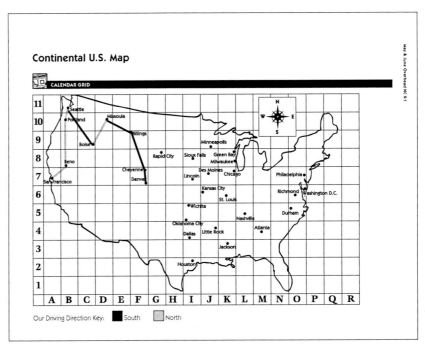

Calendar Grid Map Coordinates (cont.)

Some students may notice that the family moves from one location to the next in one direction along a single column on the map (e.g., B,8, B,10, B,11). When they have visited all the locations in that column, they reverse direction (e.g., north to south) while moving to a location in the next column to the east. Thus, the family progresses through the columns in alphabetical order (sometimes skipping a letter such as E), and the direction of travel reverses as they shift from one column to the next.

Week 3 Making Predictions

Have students work in pairs to complete Student Book pages 101 and 102, Looking Ahead & Making Predictions. The page asks students to track the family's progress from the 9th through the 18th, which may put them ahead of the markers currently posted on the calendar. If so, they will have to rely on their own map-reading skills. Remind them to pick up where they left off during the last workout to locate each city on their own map and connect the dots from city to city using the designated colors to show driving direction. This should yield the information they need to complete the chart on the worksheet and make predictions about the family's next two destinations. You'll have to decide whether you want students to name the state as well as the city when listing each destination.

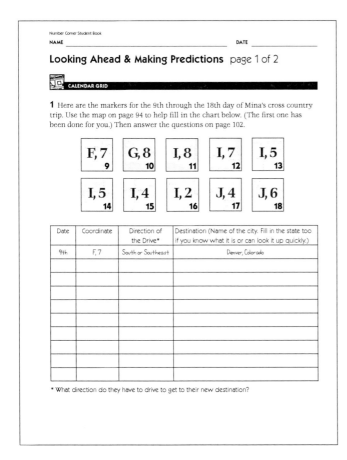

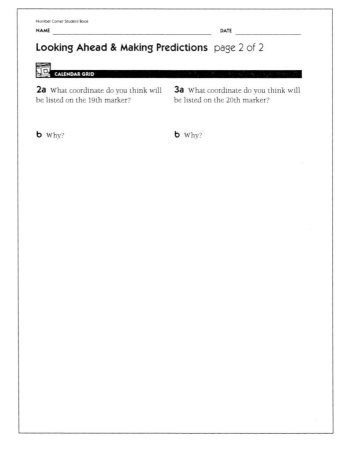

Calendar Grid Map Coordinates (cont.)

It will take most, if not all, of one Number Corner period for students to complete this page. If you can, spend time the next day having students discuss their predictions about the family's travels as a whole group. Did everyone predict the same two cities? If so, why were those locations selected? If not, have students try to convince their classmates by sharing the reasoning behind their predictions.

Week 4 Solving Story Problems about the Family's Travels

Have students complete pages 104 and 105 in their Student Books during the last Calendar Grid Workout this month. The pages include problems based on the family's travels that require students to do multi-digit calculations. If students do not complete these pages in class, consider sending them home as an assignment and then spending another workout to have students share and compare their solutions and strategies.

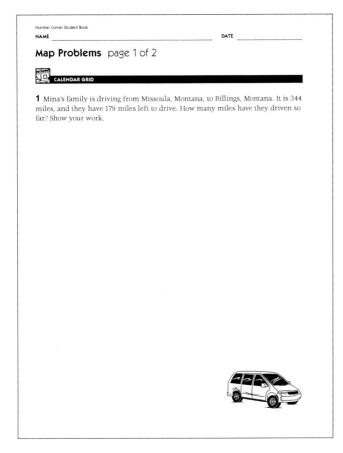

Number Corner Student Book

NAME _____   DATE _____

Map Problems page 1 of 2

▮▮ CALENDAR GRID

1 Mina's family is driving from Missoula, Montana, to Billings, Montana. It is 344 miles, and they have 179 miles left to drive. How many miles have they driven so far? Show your work.

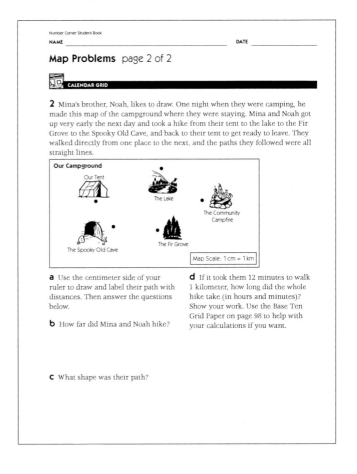

Number Corner Student Book

NAME _____   DATE _____

Map Problems page 2 of 2

▮▮ CALENDAR GRID

2 Mina's brother, Noah, likes to draw. One night when they were camping, he made this map of the campground where they were staying. Mina and Noah got up very early the next day and took a hike from their tent to the lake to the Fir Grove to the Spooky Old Cave, and back to their tent to get ready to leave. They walked directly from one place to the next, and the paths they followed were all straight lines.

Our Campground

Our Tent • • The Lake • The Community Campfire

The Spooky Old Cave • • The Fir Grove

Map Scale: 1 cm = 1 km

a Use the centimeter side of your ruler to draw and label their path with distances. Then answer the questions below.

b How far did Mina and Noah hike?

c What shape was their path?

d If it took them 12 minutes to walk 1 kilometer, how long did the whole hike take (in hours and minutes)? Show your work. Use the Base Ten Grid Paper on page 98 to help with your calculations if you want.

May & June Calendar Collector

CALENDAR COLLECTOR

Collecting Trip Miles

STUDENT BOOK

TECHNOLOGY CONNECTION

Overview

In this month's Calendar Collector, students keep a running total of the number of miles the family on the Calendar Grid travels as they make their way across the country.

Frequency

One day a week

Skills & Concepts

★ adding up to 5-digit numbers with and without regrouping

★ exploring column addition with multi-digit numbers

★ gathering information from a complex table

★ constructing a bar graph, labeling the axes, and selecting an appropriate scale

★ determining the range of a set of data

★ making and refining estimates on the basis of a growing collection of data

You'll need

★ Continental U.S. Map (Overhead NC 9.1)

★ Trip Mileage Record Sheet, pages 1 and 2 (Overheads NC 9.2 and 9.3)

★ United States Mileage Chart (Number Corner Student Book, page 95)

★ Trip Mileage Record Sheet, pages 1 and 2 (Number Corner Student Book, pages 96 and 97)

★ Graphing the Miles (Number Corner Student Book, page 107)

★ calculators

★ rulers

★ overhead pens

★ piece of chart paper

★ marking pens in several different colors

Week 1 Introducing the Trip Mileage Record Sheet & Mileage Charts

Introduce this month's Calendar Collector by displaying the overhead Trip Mileage Record Sheet. Ask students to talk first in pairs and then as a class about their observations and about what they think they will be collecting this month.

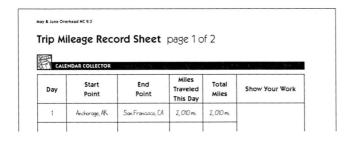

May & June Overhead NC 9.2

Trip Mileage Record Sheet page 1 of 2

CALENDAR COLLECTOR

Day	Start Point	End Point	Miles Traveled This Day	Total Miles	Show Your Work
1	Anchorage, AK	San Francisco, CA	2,010 mi.	2,010 mi.	

Calendar Collector Collecting Trip Miles (cont.)

After students have had a chance to share their observations and speculations, explain that this month they will be keeping track of the number of miles the family drives as they travel from one location to the next. They will track the daily mileage and also keep a running total for the whole trip. Ask students to find the Trip Mileage Record Sheet on page 96 in their Student Book. Work together to complete the entries through the current date. Students will find a mileage chart on page 95 in their Student Books that has the distances they need to fill in the record sheet. Departure cities are listed on the chart in alphabetical order.

Once the entries have been made, give students a few minutes to compute the running totals for each day. You'll probably need to work through the first one or two as a group to help students understand that to get the running total, they need to add each day's mileage to the total miles from the day before. There is a column on the sheet to show their computation, but some may need to use a larger sheet of scratch paper to show their figuring. (They can clip or staple scratch paper to their record sheets.) Ask students to work independently, then compare results with their neighbors, and use the calculators as a triple-check if necessary.

May & June Overhead NC 9.2

Trip Mileage Record Sheet page 1 of 2

CALENDAR COLLECTOR

Day	Start Point	End Point	Miles Traveled This Day	Total Miles	Show Your Work
1	Anchorage, AK	San Francisco, CA	2,010 mi.	2,010 mi.	
2	San Francisco, CA	Reno, NV	230	2,240 mi.	
3	Reno, NV	Portland, OR	580	2,820 mi.	
4	Portland, OR	Seattle, WA	170	2,990 mi.	

Take a few minutes now to have students estimate what they think the total mileage will be at the end of the month. Give them time to study the chart so far, and then post the U.S. Map overhead so students can see the other destination points the family will visit. As they share estimates, record them on a piece of chart paper, which you'll save for continued use throughout the month.

Teacher *Mina's father grew up in Philadelphia, Pennsylvania, so that's where the family is headed but they're planning to drive through all of the cities on the map; Philadelphia is their final destination. How many miles do you think they'll travel in all, counting the 2,010 miles they flew from Anchorage to San Francisco? Raise your hand when you have an idea, and I'll record your estimate on the piece of chart paper I've posted here.*

Students *My brother says it's about 3,000 miles across the country, but it looks like they're going to zigzag a lot.*
I think it's going to be a real lot, like 10,000.
I think it's more than that! We have almost 3,000 miles already and it's

Calendar Collector Collecting Trip Miles (cont.)

only been 4 days.

It sort of depends on what order they go to the different cities, but I'll guess 7,000.

I think more than that. If it's about 3,000 in 4 days, then I think it'll be like 7 times 3,000. 21,000 is my guess!

I think less than that. Most of the time they don't travel as much as they did when they flew that first day. I say maybe 12,000 miles.

Continue to record estimates until everyone who wants to volunteer has had a turn. Ask the class to identify and circle the highest and lowest numbers on the chart and compute the range of their estimates by finding the difference between the two. Later in the month, you'll ask students to make new estimates based on the trip mileage they've recorded by then and it will be interesting for them to see that as they gather more information, the range of their estimates tends to narrow.

....

Weeks 2–4 Continuing through the Month

Rather than having a student helper update the Trip Mileage Record Sheet each day, make the new entries and compute the running totals with the whole class once a week, using the Calendar Grid markers to determine each day's start and end point. Model the process as necessary on the overhead re-

Calendar Collector Collecting Trip Miles (cont.)

cord sheet, although many students will be increasingly able to work on their own through the month. If so, have student volunteers make the entries on the overhead to keep it up to date after they have completed their own entries.

Take a few minutes each week to return to your mileage estimate chart and encourage students to make new estimates based on the running total each week. If you record each new set of estimates in its own column, students can see the changes and will be interested to find that the range may narrow as they collect more data.

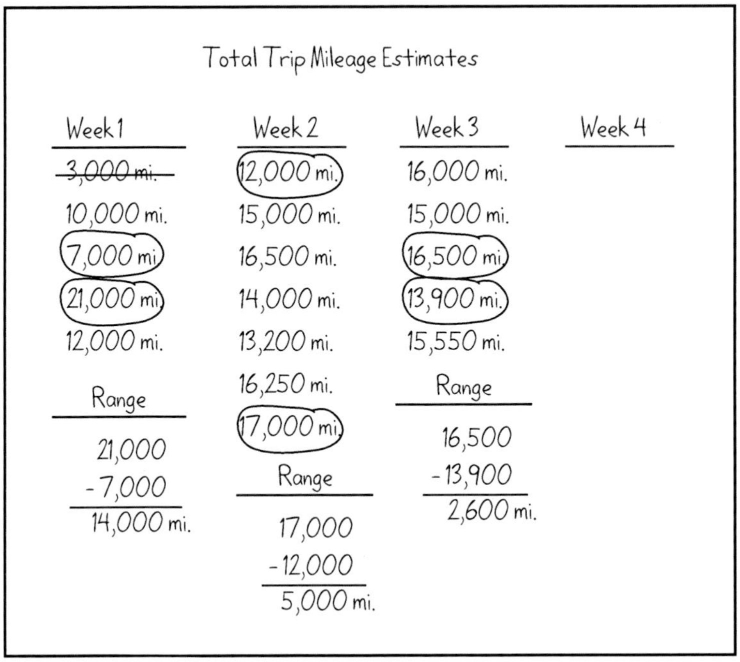

Total Trip Mileage Estimates

Week 1	Week 2	Week 3	Week 4
3,000 mi.	12,000 mi.	16,000 mi.	
10,000 mi.	15,000 mi.	15,000 mi.	
7,000 mi.	16,500 mi.	16,500 mi.	
21,000 mi.	14,000 mi.	13,900 mi.	
12,000 mi.	13,200 mi.	15,550 mi.	

Week 1 Range

$$21,000$$
$$-7,000$$
$$\overline{14,000 \text{ mi.}}$$

Week 2

16,250 mi.
17,000 mi.

Range

$$17,000$$
$$-12,000$$
$$\overline{5,000 \text{ mi.}}$$

Week 3 Range

$$16,500$$
$$-13,900$$
$$\overline{2,600 \text{ mi.}}$$

On the next page, you'll find the completed Calendar Collector record sheets to use as a reference in working with your class. Students may be amazed to find that the total number of miles traveled by the family over the course of a month is 10,658. Some of your students may be interested in calculating the average distance driven each day.

Calendar Collector Collecting Trip Miles (cont.)

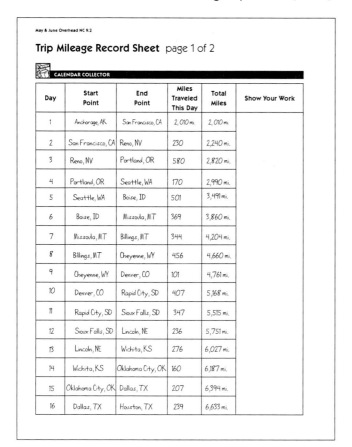

May & June Overhead NC 9.2

Trip Mileage Record Sheet page 1 of 2

CALENDAR COLLECTOR

Day	Start Point	End Point	Miles Traveled This Day	Total Miles	Show Your Work
1	Anchorage, AK	San Francisco, CA	2,010 mi.	2,010 mi.	
2	San Francisco, CA	Reno, NV	230	2,240 mi.	
3	Reno, NV	Portland, OR	580	2,820 mi.	
4	Portland, OR	Seattle, WA	170	2,990 mi.	
5	Seattle, WA	Boise, ID	501	3,491 mi.	
6	Boise, ID	Missoula, MT	369	3,860 mi.	
7	Missoula, MT	Billings, MT	344	4,204 mi.	
8	Billings, MT	Cheyenne, WY	456	4,660 mi.	
9	Cheyenne, WY	Denver, CO	101	4,761 mi.	
10	Denver, CO	Rapid City, SD	407	5,168 mi.	
11	Rapid City, SD	Sioux Falls, SD	347	5,515 mi.	
12	Sioux Falls, SD	Lincoln, NE	236	5,751 mi.	
13	Lincoln, NE	Wichita, KS	276	6,027 mi.	
14	Wichita, KS	Oklahoma City, OK	160	6,187 mi.	
15	Oklahoma City, OK	Dallas, TX	207	6,394 mi.	
16	Dallas, TX	Houston, TX	239	6,633 mi.	

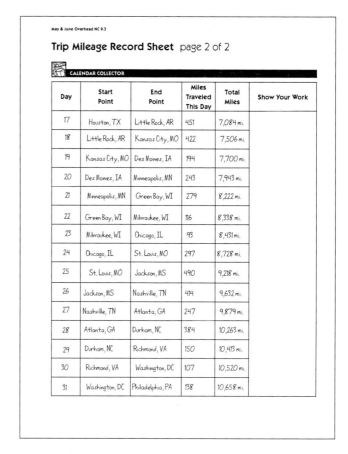

May & June Overhead NC 9.3

Trip Mileage Record Sheet page 2 of 2

CALENDAR COLLECTOR

Day	Start Point	End Point	Miles Traveled This Day	Total Miles	Show Your Work
17	Houston, TX	Little Rock, AR	451	7,084 mi.	
18	Little Rock, AR	Kansas City, MO	422	7,506 mi.	
19	Kansas City, MO	Des Moines, IA	194	7,700 mi.	
20	Des Moines, IA	Minneapolis, MN	243	7,943 mi.	
21	Minneapolis, MN	Green Bay, WI	279	8,222 mi.	
22	Green Bay, WI	Milwaukee, WI	116	8,338 mi.	
23	Milwaukee, WI	Chicago, IL	93	8,431 mi.	
24	Chicago, IL	St. Louis, MO	297	8,728 mi.	
25	St. Louis, MO	Jackson, MS	490	9,218 mi.	
26	Jackson, MS	Nashville, TN	414	9,632 mi.	
27	Nashville, TN	Atlanta, GA	247	9,879 mi.	
28	Atlanta, GA	Durham, NC	384	10,263 mi.	
29	Durham, NC	Richmond, VA	150	10,413 mi.	
30	Richmond, VA	Washington, DC	107	10,520 mi.	
31	Washington, DC	Philadelphia, PA	138	10,658 mi.	

Optional Week 5 Creating a Bar Graph

If you want to extend this workout into the month of June, assign Student Book page 107 as class work or as a homework assignment. This sheet asks students to create a bar graph to show 4 of the family's driving distances. This is a challenging exercise because students have to decide on the scale they will use to show the data (there are a number of viable options), in addition to labeling the graph and the axes properly.

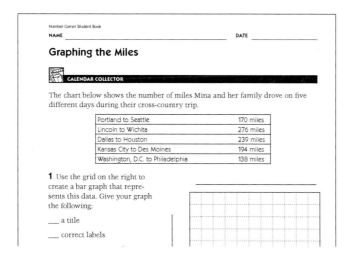

Number Corner Student Book

NAME _____ DATE _____

Graphing the Miles

CALENDAR COLLECTOR

The chart below shows the number of miles Mina and her family drove on five different days during their cross-country trip.

Portland to Seattle	170 miles
Lincoln to Wichita	276 miles
Dallas to Houston	239 miles
Kansas City to Des Moines	194 miles
Washington, D.C. to Philadelphia	138 miles

1 Use the grid on the right to create a bar graph that represents this data. Give your graph the following:

___ a title

___ correct labels

May & June Computational Fluency

COMPUTATIONAL FLUENCY

STUDENT BOOK

TECHNOLOGY CONNECTION

Roll 5

Overview

The last Computational Fluency Workout of the year is the challenging and engaging game of Roll 5, which some students may already know how to play. The game provides practice using all four basic operations in a problem-solving context.

Frequency

One day per week

Skills & Concepts

★ adding, subtracting, multiplying, and dividing numbers using mental strategies

★ applying the commutative, associative, distributive, and identity properties to calculations with whole numbers

You'll need

★ Roll 5 (Overhead NC 9.4)

★ Roll 5 (Number Corner Student Book, page 51)

★ Roll 5 Record Sheets, pages 1–3 (Number Corner Student Book, pages 52–54)

★ 1 die numbered 0–5, 2 numbered 1–6, and 2 numbered 4–9 for each pair of students

★ calculators

★ scratch paper

....

Note Students who mastered their basic multiplication facts may have played this game while the rest of the class was doing the Quick Facts routine. Those students will still be engaged, though, because the game is always different and challenging.

....

Week 1 Introducing Roll 5

To play Roll 5, each player rolls any 2 dice in a collection of 5 and then multiplies the numbers that come up. The product is the target number. The player then rolls all 5 dice and adds, subtracts, multiplies, or divides any combination of the 5 numbers to equal the target number. The player can only use each number one time, but does not have to use all 5 numbers. However, players score a point for each number they use to get to the target number, and the player with the most points at the end of the game wins. Therefore, it is to a player's advantage to use as many of the 5 numbers as possible to get to the target number. *Each number must be used as a single digit (e.g., a 6 and 2 cannot be combined to make 62 or 26).* In the unlikely event that a player cannot get to the target number with the 5 numbers rolled, he or she can roll two of the dice and multiply the numbers to get a different target number.

Computational Fluency Roll 5 (cont.)

To introduce Roll 5, display the overhead and play a full game against the students. Take your turn first and explain the rules and parameters of the game as you play your first round. When you record your 5 numbers in round 1, ask students to come up with a few ways to use the 5 numbers to get to the target number, using scratch paper and calculators if they wish. Write their ideas on the board and then record the one that uses the most numbers on the overhead, explaining that this method will earn you the most points. (If students want to show each step as a separate equation, that is fine, but do model for them how to record the sequence of computations in a single equation.)

$(6 + 4) \times (4 - 2) = 20$ 4 points
$(6 + 4) \times (4 - 2) \times 1 = 20$ 5 points
$((4 \times 4) + 6) - (2 \times 1) = 20$ 5 points
$((1 + 6) \times 4) - (2 \times 4) = 20$ 5 points

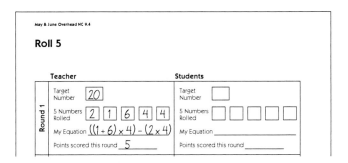

As you complete all 3 rounds, devise and share your own methods for reaching your second and third target numbers, but continue to have students share alternative methods for their numbers and choose the one that will earn them the most points. When recording different methods on the board and on the overhead, ask for student input about how to record each equation (e.g., where to place parentheses).

After completing 3 rounds, have students find the total number of points you have earned and they have earned. The player or team with the most points wins. Keep your filled-in transparency for use next week when you can use it to help students review how the game is played.

....

Weeks 2–4 Playing Roll 5 as a Class & in Pairs

At the beginning of the second workout, quickly review how Roll 5 is played by displaying and reviewing the transparency completed the first week or by having students read the instructions on page 51 of their Number Corner Student Books.

Students can use the three game sheets in their Student Books (pages 52–54) to play in pairs. (Students who have already played the game may serve as roving advisors or consultants to their classmates if you have the students play in pairs.) If it takes longer than a single Number Corner period to complete a game, Roll 5 can easily be carried over from week to week. You might also consider having students play in teams of 2 rather than one-on-one so they can support each other. Students in need of a challenge can roll the two

Computational Fluency Roll 5 (cont.)

4–9 dice to create their target numbers or generate even larger target numbers by rolling 3 dice. With Roll 5, the potential for challenge, creativity, and ongoing computational practice is nearly unlimited. You may also want to consider continuing to play with the whole group during these workouts, asking students to track the progress of both teams (teacher and class) on the record sheets in their Student Books.

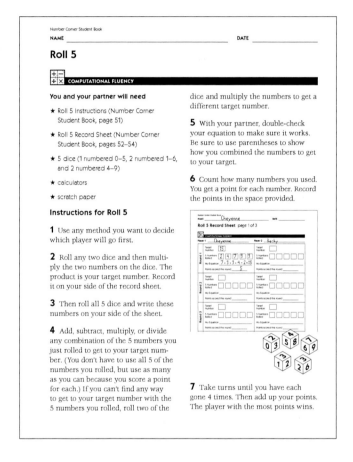

May & June Problem Solving

PROBLEM SOLVING

Travel Puzzlers

STUDENT BOOK

Overview

Like the Calendar Grid and Calendar Collector, this month's problems focus on Mina and her family as they travel across the United States. The computational emphasis continues to be on multiplication and division. Most of the problems are multi-step and feature opportunities to use such clearly defined strategies as making a table, using logical reasoning, simplifying, or guessing and checking to make the computation easier.

Frequency

One day per week

Skills & Concepts

★ adding and subtracting 2- and 3-digit numbers with and without regrouping

★ multiplying and dividing multiples of 10 or 100

★ using different models of division to solve problems

★ multiplying and dividing 2-digit numbers by 1-digit numbers

★ selecting methods and tools appropriate to a particular context for operations with whole numbers

★ solving multi-step story problems using a variety of strategies

You'll need

★ May & June Problem Solving Sheets 1–4 (Overheads NC 9.5 and 9.7–9.9)

★ Problem Solving Solution Page (Blackline NC 6.5, 4 class sets, optional)

★ May & June Problem Strips, pages 1 and 2 (Blacklines NC 9.4 and 9.5, class set cut into sections, optional)

★ May & June Problem Solving Sheets 1–4 (Number Corner Student Book, pages 99, 100, 103, and 106)

★ Base Ten Grid Paper (Number Corner Student Book, page 98)

★ a piece of paper to mask parts of the overhead when necessary

★ overhead pens and a few blank overhead transparencies

★ chart paper and marking pens (optional)

This month's problems, many of which are posed in the form of puzzles or riddles, provide students with continued opportunities to hone their communication and computation skills. All but one require that the solutions be carefully labeled with the appropriate units. Two of the problems have several different solutions. In general, the reading level is more demanding than it has been in previous months, and students will have to read each problem

Problem Solving Travel Puzzlers (cont.)

carefully to determine what they are being asked to do. Some may find it very helpful to underline or highlight the relevant information, especially in some of the longer problems.

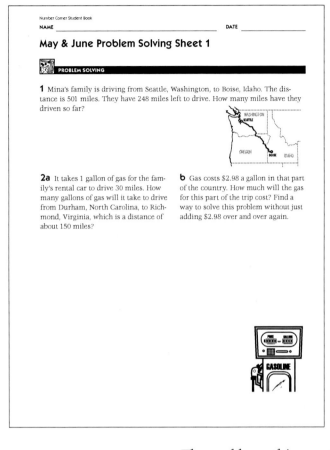

Number Corner Student Book

NAME _____ DATE _____

May & June Problem Solving Sheet 1

PROBLEM SOLVING

1 Mina's family is driving from Seattle, Washington, to Boise, Idaho. The distance is 501 miles. They have 248 miles left to drive. How many miles have they driven so far?

2a It takes 1 gallon of gas for the family's rental car to drive 30 miles. How many gallons of gas will it take to drive from Durham, North Carolina, to Richmond, Virginia, which is a distance of about 150 miles?

b Gas costs $2.98 a gallon in that part of the country. How much will the gas for this part of the trip cost? Find a way to solve this problem without just adding $2.98 over and over again.

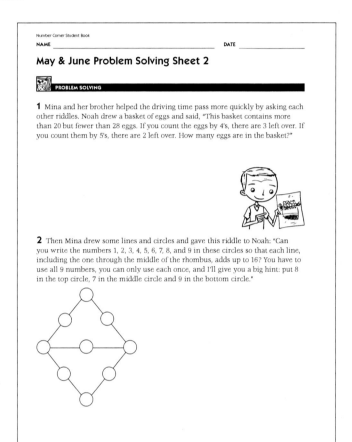

Number Corner Student Book

NAME _____ DATE _____

May & June Problem Solving Sheet 2

PROBLEM SOLVING

1 Mina and her brother helped the driving time pass more quickly by asking each other riddles. Noah drew a basket of eggs and said, "This basket contains more than 20 but fewer than 28 eggs. If you count the eggs by 4's, there are 3 left over. If you count them by 5's, there are 2 left over. How many eggs are in the basket?"

2 Then Mina drew some lines and circles and gave this riddle to Noah: "Can you write the numbers 1, 2, 3, 4, 5, 6, 7, 8, and 9 in these circles so that each line, including the one through the middle of the rhombus, adds up to 16? You have to use all 9 numbers, you can only use each once, and I'll give you a big hint: put 8 in the top circle, 7 in the middle circle and 9 in the bottom circle."

The problems this month provide opportunities to discuss various types of strategies. Although there are many ways to solve each problem, certain strategies—such as drawing a picture, making a sketch on base ten grid paper, creating a table, or finding some way to simplify the computation—really do make the most sense in some cases. The first problem on the third sheet is a good example. In this problem, the family has stopped at a fruit stand on their way through the state of Washington and purchased 16 pieces of fruit for $3.00. Apples are 25¢ each, pears are 20¢ each, and plums are 10¢ each. The quantities are low, and the numbers are easy to work with, but unless you create some kind of table to show the prices for increasing numbers of each kind of fruit, the process of finding a combination of 16 pieces that add up to $3.00 is painstakingly slow and largely hit and miss.

Problem Solving Travel Puzzlers (cont.)

Number Corner Student Book

NAME _____ DATE _____

May & June Problem Solving Sheet 3

PROBLEM SOLVING

1 Mina's family saw a fruit stand along the road as they were driving through Washington and decided to get some fruit for snacks. If they wanted to spend $3.00 and get 16 pieces of fruit, what could they buy? Can you find more than one solution to this problem?

Fruit		Price
	Apples	25¢ each
	Pears	20¢ each
	Plums	10¢ each

2 The apples were so good that the family decided to go back to the fruit stand and get more to share with the friends they were going to visit. Mina's mom came back with 3 bags full and said, "Altogether, these three bags weigh 46 pounds. Bag C weighs 20 pounds, and bag A and bag B weigh the same. How much does bag A weigh?"

Number Corner Student Book

NAME _____ DATE _____

May & June Problem Solving Sheet 4

PROBLEM SOLVING

1 The family stopped to eat their lunch beside a field with some horses and large white geese in it. As they watched the animals, Mina and Noah counted 20 feet. How many horses and how many geese might there be in the field? Give all the possible answers.

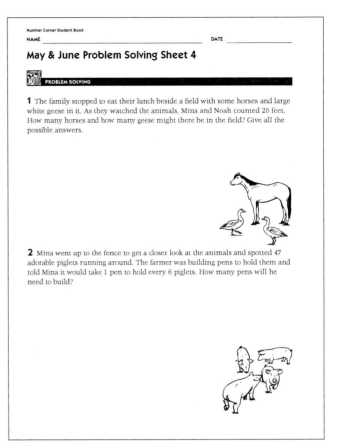

2 Mina went up to the fence to get a closer look at the animals and spotted 47 adorable piglets running around. The farmer was building pens to hold them and told Mina it would take 1 pen to hold every 6 piglets. How many pens will he need to build?

At some point early on this month, you might want to take a few minutes to have the class brainstorm a list of some of the types of problem-solving strategies that have worked for them over the year. Such a list, which you can post on a chart for reference through the rest of the month, might include:

- making a sketch or a picture on blank paper or base ten grid paper
- using or looking for a pattern
- making an organized list
- using or making a table or a chart
- thinking of some way to make the computation easier (such as rounding, estimating, or using landmark numbers)
- logical reasoning (thinking about it first)
- guess and check

Then, as you introduce a new Problem Solving sheet each week, students can be invited to identify one or more of the strategies that might be particularly helpful in solving the problems at hand.

May & June Number Line

0123 **NUMBER LINE**

What's My Number?

Overview

This month's Number Line Workout returns to the game of What's My Number?, providing students with opportunities to read, order, and compare fractions, decimals, and mixed numbers between 0 and 5. In the first workout, the class labels three number lines to prepare for a new game. In each of the three remaining workouts, the class plays several rounds of What's My Number?.

Frequency

One day a week

Skills & Concepts

★ reading, ordering, and comparing common fractions and decimals

★ locating common fractions and decimals to hundredths on a number line

★ modeling and recognizing equivalent forms of common fractions and decimals to hundredths

You'll need

★ What's My Number? (Overhead NC 9.6)

★ overhead pens in black, red, and blue

Week 1 Labeling the Number Lines

Open your first Number Line Workout by displaying the top part of the What's My Number? overhead. Ask students how the 9 marks between 0 and 5 should be labeled. This question may elicit quite a bit of discussion and debate among fourth graders, and there are 3 copies of the number line so they can label them using fractions, decimals to tenths, and decimals to hundredths. Use a black overhead marker to label each line; you'll need the red and blue markers to play the game during the other workouts. Students may test out a few ideas before settling on one that will work. As they refine their thinking, erase the labels and re-label the lines as needed.

> **Sage** *Let's just write in 1, 2, 3, and 4. We know those numbers belong in there for sure.*

> **Teacher** *Come show us what you mean, Sage.*

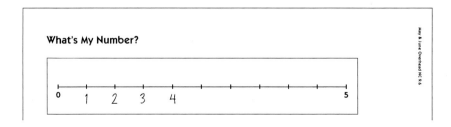

Number Line What's My Number? (cont.)

Teacher *Please take a minute to talk with the person next to you about Sage's idea. Do you agree? Disagree?*

Students *We think she's right that you need those numbers, but how she put them doesn't work.*
Maybe you could divide the last 5 marks into fractions. Like this.

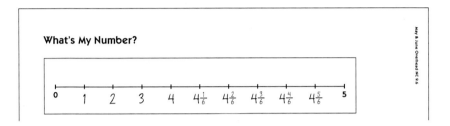

Students *That idea fills all the marks, but it doesn't seem very fair.*
Why not?
Because all the numbers with 4, like $4^1/_6$ and $4^2/_6$ take up half the number line.
We have another idea. What if you skip every other mark, like this?

Students *That seems more fair than what we had before, but not all of the marks have a number under them.*
We have an idea! What if we put halves in between the numbers?

Teacher *You mean like this?*

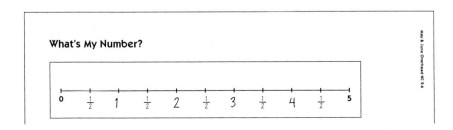

Number Line What's My Number? (cont.)

Nicole It kind of works. All the marks are filled up, and there's half between each number.

Students That doesn't make sense. Between 0 and 1 there should be half, but after that, it doesn't work to just put half.
Well, each in-between mark really is halfway between one number and then the next one.
We have another idea. Put $1\frac{1}{2}$, then $2\frac{1}{2}$, like this!

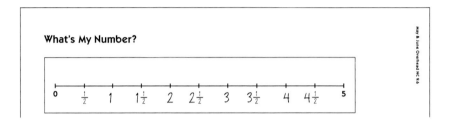

As students label the lines with fractions, decimals to tenths, and decimals to hundredths, have them use the grids at the bottom of the overhead to help see the connections between fractions, tenths, and hundredths. For example, you could ask a volunteer to shade in two of the grids to show 1 and one-half, and then have the class discuss how they can see $1\frac{1}{2}$, 1.5, and 1.50 all in the same picture.

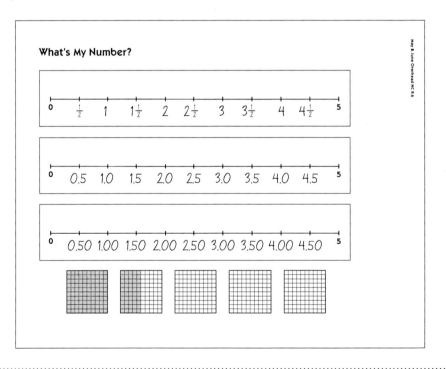

....

Note Your students don't need to label the number lines first with fractions, then with tenths, and finally with hundredths as shown here. They can do it in any order, but do make sure to have them label them in all three ways. Don't erase the transparency after your first workout. You will need it to be labeled like this for the three remaining workouts.

....

Number Line What's My Number? (cont.)

Weeks 2–4 Playing What's My Number?

In this game, you will choose a number between 0 and 5 and record it on a slip of paper in secret. It can be a whole or mixed number, a decimal or a fraction, as long as it is more than 0 and less than 5. The students will play in two teams, taking turns to guess your number and offering explanations for their guesses. Each time they make a guess, you'll have a student make a mark along the open number line to show where the number belongs. As you did if you played this game with your class in January, you will color-code your responses by recording the guesses that are *less than your target number in red*, and the numbers that are *greater than your target number in blue*. In this way, the two teams will be able to quickly narrow the range of possibilities and "zero in" on your number.

Note *Although it may seem less confusing to work with fractions and decimals separately, work with them in tandem to help students understand the connection between the two. To do so, play each round entirely on a single number line, entering decimals and mixed numbers as volunteered, even if the form used to label the number line doesn't match the form of the guess. Use the grids at the bottom of the overhead as necessary to help students see the connections between the three forms as you play the game.*

Begin by writing a number between 0 and 5 (e.g., 3.25) on a slip of paper and putting it in your pocket. Explain to the class that you have a number between 0 and 5 in your pocket, and they will play in 2 teams to try to guess that number. Tell them that teams will take turns guessing a number. Each time, you will call someone up from the team to record their team's guess on the number line. If their guess is *less* than the number, they will use a *red* pen. If their guess is *greater* than the secret number, they will record it with the *blue* pen.

Next, divide the students into two teams and determine which team will go first. Give the teams time to talk among themselves to come up with a guess. Then call on someone from the starting team. Ask her to make a mark along the number line to show where their guess belongs. If the volunteer is confused about where to place the number, invite teammates to help, using the grids at the bottom of the overhead as needed, particularly when the form of the guess does not match the form of the number line labels. If the guess is less than the secret number, ask her to record the number with the red pen. If it is greater than the secret number, ask her to record the number with a blue pen.

Alternate teams until one team guesses the secret number exactly. As they make more guesses, students will be able to narrow down the range of possibilities, and you might ask them to articulate the range of possibilities after

Number Line What's My Number? (cont.)

each guess has been made. In the example below, students can see that the number is between 2.5 and $4\frac{1}{4}$ after just two guesses. (In the example below, the guess that is less than the secret number of 3.25 is below the line and the guess that is greater is above the line.)

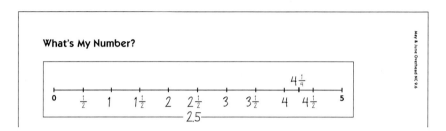

At first, students may suppose that there aren't many numbers between 0 and 5. Soon, they will probably see that there are actually all kinds of decimal and fraction numbers between 0 and 5. In the example below, the range has been narrowed to between 3 and 3.5 in a matter of only 4 guesses. The range may seem tiny, but since students are working with tenths and hundredths, there are 49 numbers between 3 and 3.5, and students may have more difficulty identifying them, making guesses that are out of the identified range at first. It will help everyone in class if you have students explain their guesses each time.

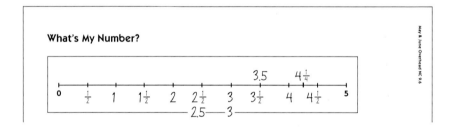

Teams may guess your number surprisingly quickly, especially after students understand how the game works. When someone guesses your number, show students the slip of paper on which you recorded it, and play the game again, using the second number line on the transparency, and then a third time, using the third number line on the transparency. Given the fragile nature of most fourth graders' understandings of fractions and decimals, you'll probably want to lead the games yourself rather than turning leadership over to the students, at least during the first workout or two. As they play, use every possible opportunity to help children make connections between the decimals, fractions, and mixed numbers between 0 and 5.

May & June Assessment

ASSESSMENT

Number Corner Checkup 4

Overview

In place of regular workouts, students spend two Number Corner periods completing a six-page skills checkup. The teacher may use a class checklist to record assessment results and get an overview of students' strengths, as well as the areas in which they need more work.

Timing

Last week of May or first week of June

Skills & Concepts

★ demonstrating fluency with multiplication and division facts

★ demonstrating an understanding of multiplication and division

★ adding and subtracting 2- and 3-digit numbers with regrouping

★ multiplying and dividing a 2-digit number by a 1-digit number

★ multiplying a 2-digit number by a 2-digit number

★ adding common fractions

★ finding factors and multiples

★ reading and ordering whole numbers to 60,000

★ reading and interpreting bar graphs, pictographs, and circle graphs

★ predicting the likelihood of an outcome numerically

★ recognizing equivalent forms of common fractions and decimals to hundredths

★ locating common fractions and decimals to hundredths on a number line

You'll need

★ Number Corner Checkup 4, pages 1–6 (Blacklines NC A 9.1–9.6)

★ Base Ten Grid Paper (Blackline NC A 9.7, class set)

★ Number Corner Checkup 4 Class Checklist, pages 1–3 (Blacklines NC A 9.8–9.10, 2 or 3 copies as needed, optional)

★ base ten pieces for students who want to use them (Use Blackline NC 1.9 to create your own base ten pieces if needed.)

Assessment Number Corner Checkup 4 (cont.)

This month includes the last of four quarterly basic skills checkups. This final checkup of the year focuses on basic multiplication and division facts; comprehension of the operations of multiplication and division; multi-digit addition, subtraction, multiplication, and division; identifying multiples and factors; ordering whole numbers; reading and interpreting bar graphs, pictographs, and circle graphs; probability; and fractions and decimals. This checkup, like the other three checkups this year, is optional. However, it can provide a good summary of what students know and can do with regard to key math skills at the end of the school year, and also provides students with another opportunity to practice test-taking skills.

Part 1 Number Corner Checkup 4, Pages 1–3

Have students complete the first three pages of the checkup during one of your regular Number Corner periods at the end of May or very early in June. Give them 2 minutes to complete as many of the 40 multiplication facts on the first page as they can. If some of your students are still gaining fluency with multiplication facts, let them know that this is just a check-in designed to help you and them see which facts they will need to work on over the summer. (It may be interesting to compare the number of facts they completed correctly this time to the number they were able to complete correctly at the end of March.) On the other hand, if most of your students are already quite fluent with their multiplication facts, you might consider eliminating this section of the checkup.

May & June Blackline NC A 9.1

NAME _____ DATE _____

Number Corner Checkup 4 page 1 of 6

1 Complete the following facts.

9 ×8	4 × 4	7 × 6	3 × 7	4 × 5	6 × 7	8 × 2

9 × 7	7 × 3	5 × 3	6 × 6	5 × 5	0 × 6	1 × 7

3 × 9	6 × 3	5 × 4	4 × 7	9 × 6	8 × 3	7 × 8

10 × 3	2 × 7	4 × 3	4 × 6	5 × 8	6 × 8	7 × 7

4 × 1	2 × 9	3 × 9	8 × 8	5 × 7	10 × 7	7 × 9

0 × 9	4 × 9	4 × 8	5 × 9	5 × 6

Assessment Number Corner Checkup 4 (cont.)

After they have had 2 minutes to work on the set of multiplication facts, give them time to complete the remaining problems on pages 2 and 3 at their own pace. Make base ten pieces and Base Ten Grid paper available to students who wish to use them.

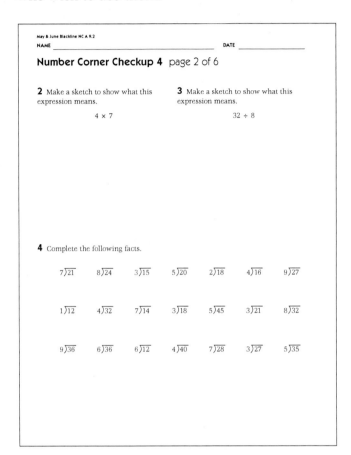

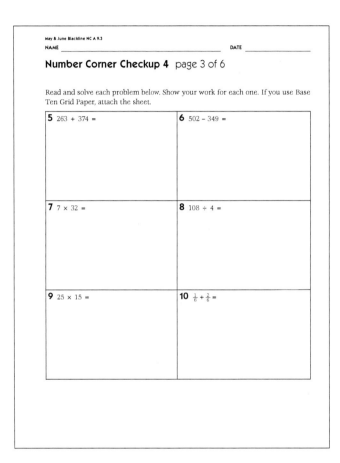

Part 2 Number Corner Checkup 4, Pages 4–6

The day after they have completed the first three pages, give students a full Number Corner period to complete the last three pages of the checkup. Again, make base ten pieces and Base Ten Grid Paper available to those who want to use them.

May & June Blackline NC A 9.4
NAME _____ DATE _____

Number Corner Checkup 4 page 4 of 6

11 Circle the numbers that are multiples of 2.

246   447   552   4,441   5,120

12 Circle the numbers that are multiples of 2 *and* 3.

12   16   21   32   36

13a List all the factors of 24.

14 Write these numbers in order on the lines below. Start with the smallest and keep going until you have used them all.

520 5,059 508 5,519 5,698 50,019

_____
_____
_____
_____
_____
_____

Assessment Number Corner Checkup 4 (cont.)

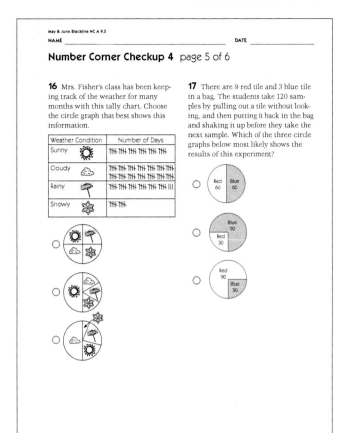

May & June Blackline NC A 9.5

NAME _____ DATE _____

Number Corner Checkup 4 page 5 of 6

16 Mrs. Fisher's class has been keeping track of the weather for many months with this tally chart. Choose the circle graph that best shows this information.

Weather Condition		Number of Days
Sunny		THL THL THL THL THL THL
Cloudy		THL THL THL THL THL THL THL THL THL THL THL THL
Rainy		THL THL THL THL THL THL THL III
Snowy		THL THL

17 There are 9 red tile and 3 blue tile in a bag. The students take 120 samples by pulling out a tile without looking, and then putting it back in the bag and shaking it up before they take the next sample. Which of the three circle graphs below most likely shows the results of this experiment?

○ Red 60 / Blue 60

○ Blue 90 / Red 30

○ Red 90 / Blue 30

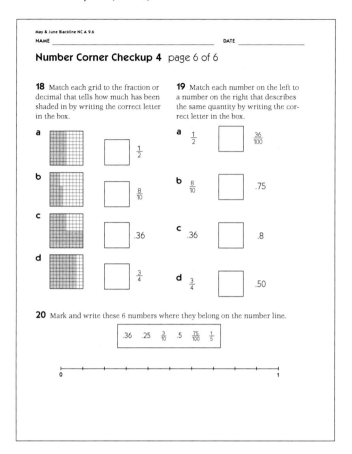

May & June Blackline NC A 9.6

NAME _____ DATE _____

Number Corner Checkup 4 page 6 of 6

18 Match each grid to the fraction or decimal that tells how much has been shaded in by writing the correct letter in the box.

a □ $\frac{1}{2}$

b □ $\frac{8}{10}$

c □ .36

d □ $\frac{3}{4}$

19 Match each number on the left to a number on the right that describes the same quantity by writing the correct letter in the box.

a $\frac{1}{2}$ □ $\frac{36}{100}$

b $\frac{8}{10}$ □ .75

c .36 □ .8

d $\frac{3}{4}$ □ .50

20 Mark and write these 6 numbers where they belong on the number line.

| .36 | .25 | $\frac{3}{10}$ | .5 | $\frac{75}{100}$ | $\frac{1}{5}$ |

0 |————————————————| 1

 SUPPORT

Support Activities

After reviewing students' responses on this final checkup, you can assign Support Activities as needed for children to work on at home. You might also make Support Activities available to teachers who are working with students in summer school or other special summer programs. We recommend creating a packet that contains the instructional considerations, instructions, and materials for these Support Activities. That way, you can simply provide summer school personnel with the packet and ask them to conduct specific activities with students who need additional work on one or more of the targeted skills. You might also choose to send one or more of the activities home with a child in need of more practice. The game instructions and materials may be enough to provide most parents with what they need to help their children, but you may find it appropriate to send home the instructional considerations as well in some cases.

Assessment Number Corner Checkup 4 (cont.)

SUPPORT ACTIVITIES		
Activity	**Name**	**Skills**
Activity 26	Round & Add Tens	Rounding 2-digit numbers to the nearest ten and adding 2- and 3-digit numbers
Activity 27	Round & Add Hundreds	Rounding 3-digit numbers to the nearest hundred and adding 3- and 4-digit numbers
Activity 28	Divide 'Em Up	Dividing 2-digit numbers by 1-digit numbers using models
Activity 29	Money, Fraction & Decimal Showdown	Comparing common fractions, decimals, and money amounts with models

May & June Answer Keys

Assessment Blacklines

Blacklines NC A 9.1–9.6, Number Corner Checkup 4

1 72, 16, 42, 21, 20, 42, 16
63, 21, 15, 36, 25, 0, 7
27, 18, 20, 28, 54, 24, 56
30, 14, 12, 24, 40, 48, 49
4, 18, 27, 64, 35, 70, 63
0, 36, 32, 45, 30

2 Students' sketches will vary. Examples:
example 1:

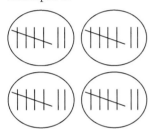

example 2:

example 3:

3 Students' sketches will vary. Examples:
example 1:

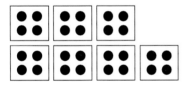

example 2:

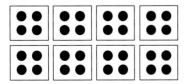

4 3, 3, 5, 4, 9, 4, 3
12, 8, 2, 6, 9, 7, 4
4, 6, 2, 10, 4, 9, 7

5 637, Students' methods will vary. Example:

$$\begin{array}{r} 500 \\ 130 \\ +\ 7 \\ \hline 637 \end{array}$$

6 153, Students' methods will vary. Example:

$$349 + \boxed{100} = 449$$
$$449 + \boxed{60} = 509$$
$$509 - \boxed{7} = 502$$
$$\overline{160 - 7 = 153}$$

7 224, Students' methods will vary. Example:
$210 + 14 = 224$

8 27, Students' methods will vary. Example:
$108 \div 2 = 54$
$54 \div 2 = 25 + 2 = 27$
so $108 \div 4 = 27$

9 375, Students' methods will vary. Example:
$25 \times 16 = 100 \times 4 = 400$
$400 - 25 = 375$

10 $3/6$ or $1/2$, Students' methods will vary. Example:

$$\frac{1}{6} \quad \frac{2}{6}$$

$$\frac{3}{6} \quad \frac{1}{2}$$

11 246, 552, 5120

12 12, 36

13 a 1, 24, 2, 12, 3, 8, 4, 6

  b Students' explanations will vary. Example:
  I started at 1 and kept going. I stopped when I got to 6, because I already did 4 times 6, so I knew I had to have them all.

14 508, 520, 5059, 5519, 5698, 50019

15 Mrs. Longchamp (20), Mrs. McCoy (34), and Ms. MacIntosh (24) together have a total of 78 students in their class.

Assessment Blacklines (cont.)

Blacklines NC A 9.1–9.6, Number Corner Checkup 4 (cont.)

16

17

Red 90 / Blue 30

18 a $^1/_2$

b .36

c $^3/_4$

d $^8/_{10}$

19 a .50

b .8

c $^{36}/_{100}$

d .75

20

.25 .36

0   $\frac{1}{5}$ $\frac{3}{10}$ .5 $\frac{75}{100}$ 1

Number Corner Student Book

pages 96 and 97, Trip Mileage Record Sheet

Day	Start Point	End Point	Miles Traveled This Day	Total Miles	Show Your Work
1	Anchorage, AK	San Francisco, CA	2,010 mi.	2,010 mi.	
2	San Francisco, CA	Reno, NV	230	2,240 mi.	
3	Reno, NV	Portland, OR	580	2,820 mi.	
4	Portland, OR	Seattle, WA	170	2,990 mi.	
5	Seattle, WA	Boise, ID	501	3,491 mi.	
6	Boise, ID	Missoula, MT	369	3,860 mi.	
7	Missoula, MT	Billings, MT	344	4,204 mi.	
8	Billings, MT	Cheyenne, WY	456	4,660 mi.	
9	Cheyenne, WY	Denver, CO	101	4,761 mi.	
10	Denver, CO	Rapid City, SD	407	5,168 mi.	
11	Rapid City, SD	Sioux Falls, SD	347	5,515 mi.	
12	Sioux Falls, SD	Lincoln, NE	236	5,751 mi.	
13	Lincoln, NE	Wichita, KS	276	6,027 mi.	
14	Wichita, KS	Oklahoma City, OK	160	6,187 mi.	
15	Oklahoma City, OK	Dallas, TX	207	6,394 mi.	
16	Dallas, TX	Houston, TX	239	6,633 mi.	

Day	Start Point	End Point	Miles Traveled This Day	Total Miles	Show Your Work
17	Houston, TX	Little Rock, AR	451	7,084 mi.	
18	Little Rock, AR	Kansas City, MO	422	7,506 mi.	
19	Kansas City, MO	Des Moines, IA	194	7,700 mi.	
20	Des Moines, IA	Minneapolis, MN	243	7,943 mi.	
21	Minneapolis, MN	Green Bay, WI	279	8,222 mi.	
22	Green Bay, WI	Milwaukee, WI	116	8,338 mi.	
23	Milwaukee, WI	Chicago, IL	93	8,431 mi.	
24	Chicago, IL	St. Louis, MO	297	8,728 mi.	
25	St. Louis, MO	Jackson, MS	490	9,218 mi.	
26	Jackson, MS	Nashville, TN	414	9,632 mi.	
27	Nashville, TN	Atlanta, GA	247	9,879 mi.	
28	Atlanta, GA	Durham, NC	384	10,263 mi.	
29	Durham, NC	Richmond, VA	150	10,413 mi.	
30	Richmond, VA	Washington, D.C.	107	10,520 mi.	
31	Washington, D.C.	Philadelphia, PA	138	10,658 mi.	

ANSWER KEY

Number Corner Student Book (cont.)

page 99, May & June Problem Solving Sheet 1

1 253 miles, Students' methods will vary.

2 a 5 gallons of gas

  b $14.90, Students' methods will vary. Examples:

  example 1:

$$\begin{array}{r} \overset{1\ 1}{2.98} \\ +\ 2.98 \\ \hline 5.96 \end{array} \qquad \begin{array}{r} \overset{1\ 1}{2.98} \\ +\ 5.96 \\ \hline 8.94 \end{array} \qquad \begin{array}{r} \overset{1\ 1}{5.96} \\ +\ 8.94 \\ \hline 14.90 \end{array}$$

example 2:

2.98 × 5 is like 3 × 5

3 × 5 = 15.00

0.02 × 5 = 0.10

15.00 – 0.10 = $14.90

page 100, May & June Problem Solving Sheet 2

1 27 eggs in the basket, Students' methods will vary.
Example:

21, 22, 23, 24, 25, 26, 27

◯   3 left if counting by 4

↑   2 left if counting by 5

I crossed out 24 because it is a multiple of 4 and 25 because it is a multiple of 5. Then I showed which ones have 3 left if you count by 4 and 2 left if you count by 5. The only one that has both is 27.

2

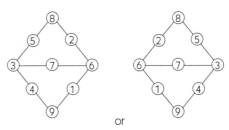

or

Students' methods for arriving at this solution will vary and many will not use words to explain their strategies. Example:

I knew that the 1 had to go with just the 9 because it's not enough with the other numbers. So I put it next to the 9. Then the 6 had to come next, because 9 plus 1 is 10 and 10 plus 6 is 16. Then I had to put a 3 after the 7, because 7 plus 6 is 13 and 3 more is 16. I kept going like that. I filled in what had to come next.

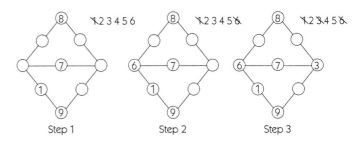

Step 1   Step 2   Step 3

pages 101 and 102, Looking Ahead & Making Predictions

1

Date	Coordinate	Direction of the Drive*	Destination (Name of the city. Fill in the state too if you know what it is or can look it up quickly.)
9th	F, 7	South or Southeast	Denver, Colorado
10th	G, 8	N.E.	Rapid City, South Dakota
11th	I, 8	S.E.	Sioux Falls, South Dakota
12th	I, 7	S.	Lincoln, Nebraska
13th	I, 5	S.W.	Wichita, Kansas
14th	I, 5	S.W.	Oklahoma City, Oklahoma
15th	I, 4	S.E.	Dallas, Texas
16th	I, 2	S.E.	Houston, Texas
17th	J, 4	N.E.	Little Rock, Arkansas
18th	J, 6	N.W.	Minneapolis, Minnesota

2 Students' predictions will vary. The 19th marker actually shows J, 7.

3 Students' predictions will vary. The 20th marker actually shows J, 9.

ANSWER KEY

Number Corner Student Book (cont.)

Page 103, May & June Problem Solving Sheet 3

1   0 apples, 14 pears, 2 plums

2 apples, 11 pears, 3 plums

4 apples, 8 pears, and 4 plums

6 apples, 5 pears, and 5 plums

8 apples, 2 pears, 6 plums

Students' methods will vary. Example:

I made a table of the prices for each fruit. Then I could look to see which prices added up to $3.00. The hard part was getting it to be 16 pieces of fruit. Also, I saw a pattern and then tried to make it go forward and backward. That was how I got the ones with 11 pears and 14 pears.

Apples	Pears	Plums
1—25¢	1—20¢	1—10¢
2—50¢	2—40¢	2—20¢
3—75¢	3—60¢	3—30¢
4—$1.00	4—80¢	4—40¢
5—$1.25	5—$1.00	5—50¢
6—$1.50	6—$1.20	6—60¢
7—$1.75	7—$1.40	7—70¢
8—$2.00	8—$1.60	8—80¢

2   13 lbs., Students' methods will vary. Example:

46 lbs. – 20 lbs. = 26 lbs.

26 lbs. ÷ 2 = 13 lbs.

pages 104 and 105, Map Problems

1   165 miles, Students' methods will vary.

2 a

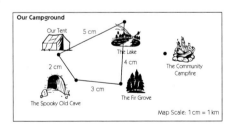

b   14 km, Students' methods will vary. Example:

5 + 4 + 3 + 2 = 5 + 5 + 4 = 10 + 4 = 14 km

c   quadrilateral (4 sides)

d   2 hours and 48 minutes; Students' strategies will vary. Example:

14 km × 12 mins. per km

14 × 6 = 60 + 24 = 84

84 + 84 = 168

168 minutes

60 + 60 = 120

1 hr.   2 hr.

168 – 120 = 48 mins.

2 hrs. and 48 mins.

page 106, May & June Problem Solving Sheet 4

1   1 horse and 8 geese (4 + 16 = 20 feet)

2 horses and 6 geese (8 + 12 = 20 feet)

3 horses and 4 geese (12 + 8 = 20 feet)

4 horses and 2 geese (16 + 4 = 20 feet)

Students' strategies will vary. Example:

Horses	Feet	Feet left for Geese	Geese
1	1 × 4 = 4	20 – 4 = 16	16 ÷ 2 = 8
2	2 × 4 = 8	20 – 8 = 12	12 ÷ 2 = 6
3	3 × 4 = 12	20 – 12 = 8	8 ÷ 2 = 4
4	4 × 4 = 16	20 – 16 = 4	4 ÷ 2 = 2
5	5 × 4 = 20	20 – 20 = 0	

I stopped here because there have to be horses and geese. These are all the answers.

2   8 pens, Students' strategies will vary. Examples:

example 1:

47 ÷ 6 = 7 R5

So they need 8 pens. There are 6 piglets in 7 pens and then the 8th pen has 5 piglets.

example 2:

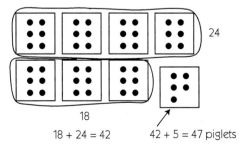

ANSWER KEY

Number Corner Student Book (cont.)

page 107, Graphing the Miles

1 Students' graphs will vary, but should include a title and labels for both axes. Example:

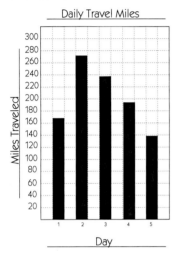

2 Students' questions will vary widely. Examples:

What was the most miles they drove in these days?

What was the shortest trip of these days?

Did they mostly drive the same amount every day, or was it very different?